972 VON   7823

Von Hagen, Victor Wolfgang,
The sun kingdom of the
Aztecs.

DATE DUE	BORROWER'S NAME	ROOM NUMBER

JAN

972 VON   7823

Von Hagen, Victor Wolfgang,
The sun kingdom of the
Aztecs.

"This re-creation of Aztec life just before the coming of the Spaniards dramatically summarizes the history, achievements, and culture of an astonishing and colorful people." — Library Journal

THE SUN KINGDOM OF **THE AZTECS**

THE SUN KINGDOM OF

THE AZTECS

BY VICTOR W. von HAGEN

ILLUSTRATED BY *Alberto Beltrán*

THE WORLD PUBLISHING COMPANY

CLEVELAND AND NEW YORK

FOR

Adriana von Hagen

WHO SHARES THE CELEBRATION OF HER SECOND YEAR OF LIFE

WITH THE BIRTH OF THIS BOOK

Published by The World Publishing Company
2231 West 110th Street, Cleveland 2, Ohio

Published simultaneously in Canada by
Nelson, Foster & Scott Ltd.

Library of Congress Catalog Card Number: 58-9419

CONTENTS

*Pronunciations for unfamiliar words
are given in the Index*

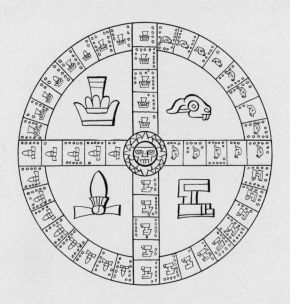

I, BERNAL DÍAZ DEL CASTILLO . . . *was off the coast of Mexico, when we discovered thickly-peopled countries inhabited by Indians. These people built masonry houses and temples, worshipped gods to whom they sacrificed human beings, cultivated cornfields and they possessed gold. When we asked for more gold . . . they pointed west in the direction of the setting sun and into the high mountains and said: "Colua, Colua, Mexico, Mexico . . ."*

On the morning of November 7, 1519 we at last reached this Mexico. We came to a broad causeway which ran miles across the lake to the center where the city of the great king Moctezuma lay. All about us we saw cities and villages built in the water, their great towers and buildings rising straight out of it. On dry land were other great towns, and with the straight level causeway leading toward Mexico it seemed like the enchantments they tell of in the legends. Some of our soldiers—we were only four hundred—even asked whether it were not all a dream. As we approached Mexico, splendidly dressed chieftains came out to meet us and they lodged us in spacious stone palaces. When I beheld all this, methought this was the garden of the world.

We proceeded on the next day along the causeway, which is here eight paces in width and runs straight to the city of Mexico. It was so crowded that we were scarcely able to pass along it. The place thronged with people and canoes, who came from all parts of the great lake to see us. This was not to be wondered at, for they had never before seen white men like us or horse or cannon.

When we arrived at the junction of the causeway . . . there came to welcome us . . . their king himself.

The Great Moctezuma approached on a litter under a marvelous canopy of green feathers embroidered in gold and silver and fringed with pearls. He was chieftain of all Mexico, of good height and slender. He wore his hair short; his manner of speaking was both tender and grave. Over two hundred chieftains were his guard

and when they went to wait upon him each gave three bows. When withdrawing they continued the bows until out of sight.

For the dining-table of Moctezuma they prepared more than three hundred dishes; they served fowl, turkeys, pheasants, quail, duck, venison and in cold weather they made a large fire in a brazier with fragrant bark. Four very beautiful women brought water for washing his hands; others, very graceful, served his meal. Fruit of all kinds was placed before him and he drank, out of a vessel of pure gold, a certain drink called chocolate.

Moctezuma had a great storehouse of weapons, of every sort and many adorned with gold and precious stones.

There were shields and two-handed wooden swords set with volcanic glass blades which cut better than our own; and lances, *and slings that hurled stones, and quilted body armour and head-gear ornamented with feathers. Moctezuma's majordomo, a fat cacique, kept his accounts of how much came in and how much went out; all the revenue was kept in books made out of paper—and so many that they filled a great house.*

In his palace there was an aviary where there was every kind of bird, from the royal eagle down to tiny hummingbirds. These were attended by three hundred Indians. When the time was right the feathers were plucked and given to the feather weavers to use for decoration. And distant from the city lived the artists. They worked in gold and made so many wonderful things that even the great goldsmiths in Spain were forced to admire them. Other artisans worked in precious stones, and there were painters and sculptors and numerous Indian women who did the weaving of fine fabrics with wonderful featherwork designs.

In other parts of the city lived Moctezuma's dancers, some who even danced on stilts and others who flew up into the air like Merry-Andrews . . . Nor must I forget to tell of the gardens of flowers and sweet-scented trees, irrigated by canals of running water and the baths made of cut stone with places to sit.

At their markets we were astonished at the number of people and the vast quantity of merchandise. Each ware, each thing to sell had its fixed place; gold, silver, precious stones, feathers, robes, chocolate, skins, sweet potatoes, and rope. Even Indian slaves were for sale with their necks tied with long poles.

In another part they sold vegetables and herbs, fruit and fowl. And there was honey and lumber and firewood and those who sold copper knives and gold dust, which they put in goose-quills so that it showed through, and gourds full of seeds they called chocolate. The things sold were so numerous and the market so crowded with people that I could not see it all in less than two days.

Then we ascended the great pyramid. This temple, the greatest in Mexico, was raised to their god—the Hummingbird Wizard— and it is so large that the circuit of the temple itself was equal to that of six large house lots. From the base it narrowed to a flat summit reached by a hundred and fourteen stone steps. When we reached the summit we saw the sacrificial stone; there was a huge figure like a dragon and other idols, and about it much fresh-spilled blood.

The temple stood so high that from it one could see over everything. We saw the three road-causeways that led from the main-

land to the city—since Mexico is an island in the middle of the great lake—and we could see the great aqueduct which supplied the city with the finest water where it came out of Chapultepec forest. We beheld on that great lake a multitude of canoes loaded with provisions. We saw in these cities temples all gleaming white and wonderful to behold. The noise and hum from the market place *below us could be heard more than two miles distant. Those of our men who had been at Rome and at Constantinople said that for arrangement, order and population, they had never seen the like ...*

Such was the capital of the Aztecs in 1519, as seen through the eyes of the first Spaniards to arrive in Mexico. The Aztecs held more than half of that great land under dominion. Their territory was so large that Cortés, conqueror of the Aztecs, confessed to the King of Spain: "The whole of it is so large that I am unable to find out exactly the extent of Moctezuma's kingdom." They did know, for they saw it written in books of picture-writing, that the Aztecs had 371 other tribes and villages under tribute.

How had this happened?

Who were the Aztecs, and how had they conquered so much of Mexico? How did they make their lives so luxurious that old soldiers who had seen Rome and Constantinople swore they had never seen anything like Mexico in all their lives?

In this lies their history.

THE LONG-AGO PEOPLE

SPEAKING EAGLE, although only fourteen years of age, knew something of Aztec history. He knew how the Aztecs had become great. For he, like all other Aztec boys, attended a clan-district school. There old men, wise in things of life, told them who the Aztecs were and how they had come to be.

The clothes the boys wore were all alike, for to dress well was to dress like everyone else. Even though it was surrounded by snow-topped volcanoes, days were warm in Mexico. All one wore was a breechclout, a sort of cotton belt that wound about the waist, and a cloak. The cloak was of woven cotton, beautifully done with images of animals or plants worked into it, and since the Aztecs had neither buttons nor pins, it was tied at the shoulder.

Speaking Eagle belonged to the Yopica clan, as did all the other boys who attended this clan school. There were twenty such clans in Mexico, each with its own district, its own school, and its own temple. These clans made up the Aztec tribe. The clan was a group, large or small, who were united together by blood ties; Speaking Eagle was related, in one way or another, to all the members of his clan, even though they might number more than 20,000 people.

14

The clan owned land which it loaned to each member. On this each man grew the crops which fed his family. Much care was taken to make sure that a large family would have enough land to feed all the people in it. There was rank without class. The clan, advised by its old men, who were elected by vote, ran the district. The old men also operated the clan school. It was there that Speaking Eagle, like the rest of the boys, learned the history of his people.

The old men read about it from books. The pages were folded and made of *amatl*, a paper which was made by beating the soft inner bark of the wild fig tree until it had the feel of thick cloth. Speaking Eagle knew this because his father had often been on journeys to the warmer lands below Mexico and had seen how it was done. The thick paper was whitened with a gum, heated, and pressed with hot stone irons. On this, men who understood the mysteries of writing painted symbols of houses, turkeys, deer, smoke, or obsidian knives and formed them into "speaking pictures."

After the boys of the clan had lessons in the use of the bow and arrow and the lance, and practiced the use of the sling (which they were taught by an old warrior) they would sit on a *petate,* a mat plaited from dried grass, and listen as the old teacher told of the "long-ago people."

No one was exactly sure how long ago it was. Nor did they exactly know how people came to this land. But they came. Sometime, perhaps as long ago as 40,000 years, America and Asia were linked by land. A land bridge connected one continent with the other. Over it went the animals, and over it came man. He came wrapped in skins against the cold and hunted the animals. In time he learned to find and select plants, and in time these plants became corn, potato, squash, and tomato. In time and with time, the men who came to America over the Alaskan land bridge became separated into tribes with different kinds of speech and different dress and different gods.

In Mexico and south of Mexico were the Maya. They built great temple cities of stone and lived in the hot lands. They began more than 3,000 years before the Aztecs. Even while Speaking Eagle and the other boys of the clan were hearing of the long-ago people they knew that the Maya still lived somewhere to the south.

Then there were the Olmec. They were those who lived in the direction of the rising sun, that is, to the east in the hot lands of the Gulf Coast. They were mysterious people. No one could even say what they looked like. When Aztec warriors walked through ancient Olmec lands they saw gigantic stone-carved heads, seven feet tall, squatting in the jungle. As the Aztecs began to conquer cities further south, they found more evidence of the Olmec. In Oaxaca, which was filled with temples, there were large cities on the hills overlooking the valley. There the Aztecs found the Olmec again! Speaking Eagle knew this to be true because his grandfather, who was a warrior and fought with the clan to capture that city, had seen the strange drawings carved on the walls. They had large round heads, flat noses, and slits for eyes.

Many different tribes such as these lived long, long before the Aztecs. They, too, had built large temple cities. On the walls of their pyramids were paintings of their life here on earth and as they imagined it to be in the hereafter. They had played a game with a rubber ball—a game like basketball—just as the Aztecs did. So Speaking Eagle knew that many of the things that were a part of Aztec life had been invented long before.

Other long-ago people lived in the jungles on the warm Gulf Coast where there were monkeys and parrots. They called themselves the Totonac, and their region was called the hot lands, for it rained much and trees grew tall. These people often became ill from fevers which they believed came out of the jungles. They too built temple cities of stone, they had ball courts, and there were mural paintings on their buildings, just like the Aztec. Some of the Totonac tribes still lived in the hot lands.

The famous Toltec tribe had built their ancient cities very near the Totonac. No one knew what the Toltec had called themselves. They were gone, and only a memory of them was left before the Aztec came. Yet only forty miles from the Aztec island city of Mexico was the valley of Teotihuacán, and in it there were great mounds. "Temples," said the old teacher, reading his book to make him remember the better. "Temples, the largest and tallest in the whole Mexican land."

The Toltec were the greatest of all the long-ago people. They began a thousand years before the Aztec. They perfected writing. They had folded books. They wove beautiful robes in cotton which they got from other tribes in the hot lands. And they were master builders. Their temples and cities were greater than any of those before them. Any Aztec who was a good sculptor or a good painter or an artist was called a Toltec.

The Aztec inherited all they had from these long-ago people. The old schoolteacher did not deny it.

When did the Aztec begin?

The old man knew the exact date. It was in the Aztec year 2-Cane, that is, 1168. It was written very plainly in the folded books. The date had been handed down from father to son and when the Aztecs began to write, it was remembered and set down.

Some believe that the Aztecs had their origin in the far north, that is, out of Arizona; others say they came from the fabled land of Aztlan, but no one knows where this place really was. But in any case, said the old man, tradition had it that the Aztecs began in 1168. It was then that they became aware of who they were, and it was then that the clans formed a tribe and began to wander south looking for land.

All the good lands were already filled, of course, and the tribes that lived on them did not want the Aztecs to settle on

their lands or to grow corn and squash, chili peppers and beans on them. So the Aztecs moved from place to place, going always in the direction of the great Mexican lakes—the fabled land of Anáhuac.

There were not many Aztecs then, not more than a thousand. Even though they were proud and very warlike they were still too small a number to fight people all the way to the lakes. They had no cotton and no wool, so the women spun the fiber of the maguey plant into thread and wove garments from it. They had no books and no one knew anything about writing. Their god was called Hummingbird Wizard. They carried his image everywhere before them, and wherever they camped they set it up. One night, it is said, the idol spoke to them.

"Look for lands, and avoid fighting," it said. "Send pioneers ahead, and have them plant land with corn and squash and beans. Then when the harvest is ready, move up to that land. Keep doing that until you reach some land which is not taken. Carry me, the Hummingbird Wizard always before you; feed me on human hearts from warriors taken in battle who are sacrificed before me."

All of which the Aztecs did.

Was it true that the Hummingbird Wizard spoke? Yes, the god spoke in a god's speech which is not ours, but still it tells us the secret longing of our hearts. When this is true, we hear it.

After the year 1168, the Aztecs came to the valley of the lakes of Mexico.

At this point in the history, the wise old teacher showed the boys the pages in the book that told how the Aztecs arrived. The boys crowded about him as he turned the leaves. They could see the footprints there, crossing the page. That, they knew, meant a journey. And there were the chiefs of the tribe carrying their belongings on their backs. Above their heads was a drawing—a sort of coat of arms—which told the name of each clan of the tribe.

The lakes of Mexico had five names, but in truth all of them were only one large lake that was more than fifty miles long. Around it were high mountains and volcanoes. Two of them were snow-covered the year round. In the day it was warm; at night, because it was over 7,000 feet above sea level, it was cold. Around the edge of the central lake, called Texcoco, there were many cities, some of which were built of stone. Each city was like a state, and each was occupied by different people of different speech. Each city had its own customs, too, although all the people worshiped gods of the earth, of the sky, and of plants. And all were enemies of each other.

The Aztec tribe set up camps around the shores of the lake. They cleared the land of some of the big cypress trees and made simple houses of sun-dried brick with thatched roofs of grass. They raised a temple and in it put Huitzilopochtli, the Hummingbird Wizard God. They began milpas, small plantations of corn. These were tended by both the women and the men; into each hillock of earth they put three grains of corn and a dead fish, which was fertilizer. Later, after the corn came up, they planted climbing beans in the same hill; the beans would use the cornstalk to grow on. Still later, they planted squash. This is how the Aztec people came to the lakes of Mexico.

Then the wars began.

At the word "wars" the boys rushed forward to see the war-history pictures. These showed the Aztec warriors with long spears fighting with other tribes and burning their temples. They did not always win. They lost many times, and for a long time the Aztecs were held as slaves by the people who conquered them.

Speaking Eagle knew well all this part of the history. His grandfather had known how to read the books. Speaking Eagle remembered the tales of the long-ago people that his grandfather, when he was still living, had told them at night and his story of how the Aztecs had escaped from slavery.

One night all the warriors of the Aztec who were held in slavery had gathered their families together and quietly moved

to the Chapultepec forest. There, among the towering great trees, they had hidden the canoes they had made when their overlords were not looking. As quietly as possible they pulled their canoes to the edge of the lake. And then in the quiet of the night, lit by a thousand stars and with the moon shining on the eternal snows of "Popo," the volcanic mountain Popo-catepetl, the warriors paddled out to two small islands in the center of Lake Texcoco, more than five miles from shore. When they arrived, other Aztecs who had come from a different part of the mainland were already there. Before their captors even knew what had happened—that the Aztecs had escaped, or where they had gone—the tribe was safe on the islands.

All this happened in the year 1321, and all of it had been arranged by secret plan. Speaking Eagle always remembered with pride that his own clan, the Yopica, had been one of the first to leave the mainland.

There was not room for everyone on the tiny islands. In the first years the Aztecs built houses of lake reeds woven together like baskets. On these they pressed a prepared soft mud that in time would harden like cement. They used long grass knitted strongly together to make roofs for the houses. Every part of the marshy land was used to cultivate corn and beans, squash and chili peppers. Then, when there was no more land, the Aztecs made *chinampas*.

Every Aztec boy knew what a *chinampa* was. Speaking Eagle, following his father's instruction, had made his first one when he was only eight years old. First, they wove reeds into a big basket, oval in shape and eight feet in diameter, and put a layer of strong leaves in the bottom of it. Then the basket was anchored to the shallow lake bottom at the edge of the island and filled with earth scooped out of the bottom of the lake. This step was a favorite one with the boys, who loved to dive under the water to bring up the rich muck. When the *chinampa* basket was filled and the earth in it had dried, the Aztecs planted corn and beans and other plants in it.

Mexico is tropical land, and the plants in the *chinampas* grew quickly. Soon trees and bushes pushed their roots through the wickerwork of the basket down into the lake bottom. In a short time the *chinampa* was firmly anchored in place.

Hundreds and thousands of these garden baskets were made and used near the islands. After a while, the islands were enlarged by them and became one. When an Aztec had ten *chinampas* wedged together, the land he had made was big enough to put his house on a piece of it. Each group of these floating gardens was separated from others by canals. That is how the Aztec city grew.

Four years later, in 1325—the Aztec year 2-House—the Aztecs came together in a great square in the center of their island city to dedicate their pyramid-temple, called Teocalli. It was not large then, the old teacher told the boys, who had to see again and again the steps of stone and the temple on top of it as it was drawn in the books. It was modest in size, like the small island and the small number of people themselves who had made their city with their own hands. On that day the city of Mexico was dedicated. The Aztecs called it Tenoch-titlán, because the city was filled with cactus, and their word for this plant was *tenoch*. They called themselves Tenochas, the people of Tenoch—and their city became Tenochtitlán, Place of the Cactus.

Year after year the Aztecs worked to build up their island. Soon they began to sell their products to other tribes on the mainland. They had discovered that one end of their lake was very saline because the water from the lake had no outlet. They learned to draw out this salt and sell it. The Aztec also

learned to work with his hands as a skilled craftsman. He made
mirrors out of the black volcanic glass, or obsidian, that he
found at the edge of the great volcanic mountains and polished
them until they shone like glass. He learned to make strong
bows and arrows, and he perfected a spear point of obsidian
with edges so sharp that it could cut like a razor.

There were occasional wars, and slowly the Aztecs began to
acquire land on the shores of the lake. This land was cultivated
by tribesmen who paddled daily from the island to the shore
in canoes. Now the tribe was growing. Water protected them
from attack, and soon they were strong enough to battle
against strong enemies. Soon all the other tribes that lived
around the lake felt the Aztec strength. By the year 1400 all
the land that lay about the lake and well back from it was in
Aztec hands.

It was then that one of the great leaders whom the Aztecs called First Speaker instead of king built the first bridge to the mainland.

"The time has come to link us to the lands of Anáhuac," Huitzilhuitl, for such was his name, told the council of old men. What he meant was clear: The capital city of Tenochtitlán must be bridged to the mainland. But how? Well, they had canoes, said Huitzilhuitl. Let there be brought 2,000 such canoes—and he wrote the symbol for 2,000 on a large piece of paper and had his artist draw a canoe on it. This was passed around the council so that all present could see how many dugout canoes each section of the city had to furnish. "Then when the canoes are in place, anchor them to the shallow bottom. Now, lay planks of wood on top of them. That will be the bridge." Later the workmen could replace the canoes with *chinampas*, anchor them to the lake, and run the bridge on top of them. Then it would be secured.

At first the old men of the council did not believe it was possible to build a bridge, but the younger men were filled with ambition and the desire to make their city the fairest of all. They said it could be done. And so it was. Tenochtitlán, capital of the Aztecs, was connected with the mainland by a pontoon bridge that was three miles long. That was only the beginning. Now, as Speaking Eagle knew, there were four causeways to the mainland, each one leading toward one of the four cardinal directions: north, south, east, and west.

The Aztec leaders thought of the comforts of the people, for the city was growing continuously. Everything in the city had to have order. At first, fresh water for the people had come from springs on the islands. But when the city grew larger, the Aztecs had to bring drinking water from the mainland in canoes. This took too much time, so they decided to build an

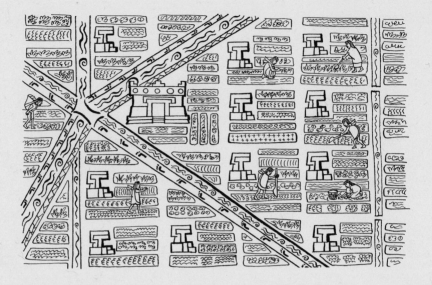

aqueduct. This was another giant causeway, a pontoon bridge that connected the city of Mexico with Chapultepec forest on the mainland.

This was the forest that had sheltered the Aztec before he founded his city. Here, trees grew to great heights, and were so big that twenty men holding hands could not encircle the trunks of the largest trees. Springs of fresh water gushed from the ground in this forest. This is how the Aztecs built the aqueduct between Chapultepec and the city.

In the year 1440 the Aztec leader was Itzcoatl, which means Snake Blade. He brought together the great council. They came to his palace, whose walls were hung with beautifully woven cotton tapestries. The councilors drank chocolate from golden cups, and charcoal braziers burned brightly in the center of the room to keep out the chill. Itzcoatl, who as First Speaker was leader of the council, spoke first.

The city had to have a better water supply. To bring water to the city by canoes was time consuming, and to have men or women bring it across the bridge from the forest of Chapultepec in large earthen jars carried on their backs was also too long a journey. They must build a giant aqueduct. To explain how it was to be done, Itzcoatl's artist, who sat beside him, drew a picture of the pontoon bridge; then he added to it the Aztec symbol for water and drew pictures of the pipes that would carry the water.

All the council fell to talking, for this was a greater task than building the first causeway to the mainland had been. Everyone argued how it was to be done. Then Itzcoatl said, "Let it be done with mud as we make our pottery."

Immediately, everyone knew what he meant. The Aztecs made all their own dishes of earthenware. They molded them in clay, painted them, and then hardened them in fire. They also knew how to make large ornate decorations for their temples by this method. There was no reason they could not make the hollow pipes for the aqueduct too. They decided the pipes should be made of clay, that they should be as thick as a man's body, and that each pipe should be cast in such a way that it could be joined to another without danger of leaking through the joint. Still, a pipe five miles long! Was this not asking too much of a people who only two hundred years ago were wandering hunters? But nothing was too great or too small for the Aztec to do. So it was done.

Within two years, there was not one, but two great ceramic pipes as thick as a man's body running the length of the bridge into Chapultepec forest. Soon fresh water was available in all parts of the city. It was piped into fountains where, as Speaking Eagle well knew, the women went each morning and night to

fill the large red water jars which they took back to their homes.
All the boys in the clan school knew about this great feat of
the Aztecs. It made them proud of their people.

The Aztec tribe was now the greatest in the land. They
feared no one. They had so great an army that they could
afford to open their island capital to everyone, inviting them
to come across the four causeways that joined it with the mainland. The tribes around the lake who were once enemies of
the Aztecs were now their friends. Every day brought new
victories. Aztec warriors had conquered all of the people south
of the lakes of Anáhuac as well as those to the east, one hundred
miles across the mountains, who lived in the hot lands along
the shore of the Totonac land where there were monkeys and
jaguars, long-tailed birds and crocodiles.

Beyond this shore was the sea—the great lake, the Aztecs

called it. They never sailed it, for they were mountain-dwelling Indians and were afraid of the sea. But all of the hot lands, stretching for hundreds of miles to the north and hundreds of miles to the south, were dominated by the Aztecs. There was an Aztec fortress every hundred miles along the coast.

Now Moctezuma was the First Speaker of the Aztec tribe, and at the mention of his name every Aztec boy shivered slightly in fear and respect. Every time Moctezuma passed, the Aztec had to bow and look to earth. One must never look into his eyes. He lived with his guards and his household in a palace near the great square where the market was held and where the giant pyramid stood. Inside the palace he had a zoological garden where specimens of all the birds of the realm and the wild animals that roamed the jungle were kept.

"One must not fear Moctezuma," the old teacher told the boys. "He is not a god. One must love and respect him as our leader."

Speaking Eagle realized this was so. Moctezuma, like all the chiefs of the Aztec, had been elected First Speaker. Yet he also knew that Moctezuma's word could mean life or death. So, although he and all the boys respected him, they also feared him.

As Speaking Eagle looked out of the door of the school and beyond he could see people busy at their work; some were fishing, others bringing produce to the markets in canoes. He could see the tall snow-covered volcano Popocatepetl rising high into the heavens, with only the thinnest plume of smoke coming out of its crater. It was peaceful and at rest, as was all the Mexican land beyond the city. The conquered tribes were quiet, working as they had always done to give their tribute to the Aztec every six months. When the tribute was collected, it was brought to the city and the city grew in riches and beauty. No one in this wide and beautiful land dared to raise his voice against the Aztec Moctezuma. All was well, except . . .

Except that something was happening out on the ocean-sea. No one yet knew what it was, but it was whispered in the houses, and Speaking Eagle had heard his father talking about it in hushed tones with other men who came to their house in the quiet of the evening. Something was going on out there on the sea. Strange men in strange ships kept appearing and disappearing along the warm coast in the Totonac land. Speaking Eagle's father said it had been going on since the year after Speaking Eagle was born. The Aztec heard of these strange men in 1502, when they first appeared; now they were back again. Some people thought it was the Plumed Serpent God returning to Mexico, that he was coming back as he said he would one day. The priests thought so too, and all through the days and nights they were offering prayers to the gods, looking into their horoscopes, and consulting the ancient writings to see if the Plumed Serpent's prophecy was coming true.

Speaking Eagle had learned about the Plumed Serpent God almost as soon as he learned the name of his mother. The Plumed Serpent was everywhere on the land. His picture was everywhere. His image was drawn on the walls of the schools where Aztec boys learned to be Aztec priests, and it appeared on the highest of the temples. It was carved in stone on the temple steps. The Plumed Serpent God wore a bird's mask with a snake's mouth—a wide-open mouth showing all the teeth and fangs of a snake—and from his head waved the most beautiful feathers in the world, the green-gold feathers of the quetzal bird. When Moctezuma and his chieftains were dressed in their finest, they wore headdresses of green-gold quetzal feathers that reached almost to the ground.

Who was this serpent god whom the Aztec called Quetzal-coatl? Before he became a god he was a man—a king or a chieftain—of the Toltec people who lived a thousand years before the Aztec. The Toltecs were great builders and wonderful craftsmen; remains of their temples could still be seen in the valley of Teotihuacán—the Place of the Gods. Quetzalcoatl—the name means Plumed Serpent—built the city of Tula, a wonderful stone city decorated with carved serpent heads and quetzal plumes. And in the city there was a hall of warriors with his own carvings of stone warriors on all the pillars. So far-famed was the city of Tula that Quetzalcoatl was revered as a god. Even his birthday, the year 1-Reed, was celebrated.

The pictorial histories say he warred with another god, who had the strange name of Smoking Mirror. The Plumed Serpent God was a kind god; he was the genius of the winds and the god of knowledge. He was against human sacrifice. He thought that one could understand nature better by studying it than by sacrificing human beings on the temple altar to enlist the aid of the gods against nature. So the Plumed Serpent warred with Smoking Mirror, who thought just the opposite.

No one knew exactly whether these men were really mortals

who fought over the kingship of Tula or if they were really gods. Perhaps the priests changed history into fable so that the simple people could understand it better. Speaking Eagle's father, who was very wise in these things, for he had traveled as a warrior all over the land and had seen the ruins of Tula with his own eyes, said: "The Plumed Serpent, whom we call Quetzalcoatl, was first a man. He lived in Tula in the year 1080, at the time that our people, the Aztec, were beginning to know who they were and before we had cotton mantles or writing or temples."

There was a civil war between Quetzalcoatl and Smoking Mirror, and Quetzalcoatl was forced to leave his land. He was sent into exile, and many of his warriors went with him. They wandered southeast until they came to the Mixtec tribe who, hearing of Quetzalcoatl's greatness, invited him to come to their capital called Cholula. There he stayed, and there he directed the building of the tallest pyramid-temple in all Mexico, a temple so high that it was called Man-made Mountain.

Quetzalcoatl built the ball court at Cholula and showed the people how to play the sacred ball game with rubber balls. He also taught them to write in the pictorial language of Mexico. But Smoking Mirror, still his enemy, would not let him rest in peace. Perhaps he threatened to make war on the Mixtec and tear down their great temple if they allowed the Fair God to reside there any longer. Perhaps there were other reasons why Quetzalcoatl left the land of the Mixtec, for who knows the ways of the gods? They are inscrutable. Whatever the cause, Quetzalcoatl and all his warriors who would not stay behind left that land where he had lived and traveled to Xicalango on the sea.

Xicalango was an ancient trading center on a great lagoon

where the Indians from Mexico and Yucatan, from Honduras, and from other places hundreds of miles around came to exchange goods. Speaking Eagle knew the name well, for the big white shell which he used to put to his ear to hear the roar of the sea came from there. Even when there was war between the tribes, a truce was declared at Xicalango so the people could trade with one another. It was custom that all arms must be left outside the trading center; people coming there to bargain this for that came in peace. Xicalango was the only place where the Maya, a great tribe that lived in Yucatan where they built immense stone cities so tall that they rose above the trees of the jungle, would talk to the Aztec. For the two tribes hated each other, and it was only because they lived so far from each other that war was impossible between them. But here the Maya and the Aztec traded and talked together. And so to this place came Quetzalcoatl and his warriors.

There was a civil war raging in Yucatan at that time, and the Maya were looking for warriors. They knew the reputation of the Toltec fighters who used the great bow and arrow and who could throw arrows from an *atlatl*, a spear thrower, with so much force that they could go right through a man. Some of the Maya chieftains came to powwow with the warriors. If they agreed to come as hired soldiers and fight on their side, they told the Toltec, and if they defeated the other Maya fighters, they would be rewarded.

No one knew exactly what happened after that. The Toltec warriors accepted, but many believe that Quetzalcoatl did not. Instead he built a large dugout canoe and prepared to sail out into the ocean-sea. Was he sailing to his death because he could not make all the tribes come together as brothers? Was he sad because he could not make them see the uselessness of human sacrifice? There is no answer. But according to all the traditions set down in picture books, he told the people, "I am sailing away, but some day—on the day of my birth which is 1-Reed—I will return and re-establish my ancient kingdom in Mexico."

After he was gone, he became a god in the Aztec pantheon —the god of the winds and the god of learning. He was many things and all things to all men. And now . . .

What were these strange portents? Who were these strange men with beards and white skins, whose strange ships appeared and disappeared along the coasts of Mexico? The priests had made calculations from their books and horoscopes and calendars that the year 1-Reed, the year in which Quetzalcoatl had said he would return, could only fall in the years 1467 or 1519. And the year 1519 was now only four years away . . .

THE MILPAS

THE beating drums, sounding like thunder until the booming of the shell horns began, wakened them, and Speaking Eagle opened his eyes. Another day had begun. Each dawn, even while stars still commanded the sky, the people of Mexico were awakened by the drums and conch horns of the temples. The drumming began first in the great Teocalli at Tenochtitlán; then it was picked up by temple after temple throughout the city.

Like most Aztec houses, there were only two rooms in the home of Speaking Eagle's family. One was the sleeping quarters where the whole family slept together on a bed made of a raised bank of earth and covered with a *petate*, or grass mat. Their blanket was a coarsely woven cotton mantle. The floor of this room was stamped earth which hardened in time like cement, and on it skins were sometimes spread. In one corner was a chest of woven *petate* where the family kept their valued things; and on the walls of the room were fishing nets, spears, and clothes, all hung on pegs.

The other room of the house was a kitchen. By dawn the mother and sisters were already preparing the food there. On the floor was a metate, a stone mortar used to grind corn to make bread. To work it, one had to get on one's knees.

35

Grinding corn was women's work. Men never did it, although it was a slow, laborious chore. First, the corn was steeped in lime ash which caused the kernel to swell and soften. Then it was boiled in a large red earthen jar until the husk peeled off. Finally, the soft white corn was put on the metate-mortar and ground with a stone roller which was cleverly made to fit the exact shape of the mortar. When the corn was twice ground, a piece of the corn mass was scooped up and patted into pancake-shaped tortillas as large as a water lily. Now the corn cake, or tortilla, was ready for the *cumal*, or oven, which stood near the metate. On it the corn cakes were baked, first on one side and then deftly turned to bake on the other.

These corn cakes, called *tlaxcalli*, were the main part of every Aztec meal. They were their bread. They also served as knives and forks, for of such implements the Aztecs had none. Instead, they piled boiled black beans or pieces of deer meat on the corn cakes, rolled them up, and ate them.

As a boy of fourteen Speaking Eagle was allotted two large *tlaxcalli* a day. He remembered that when he was four years old, he had been allowed only half a corn cake a day. When he was as old as his father he would get four large ones.

At the first breath of day the women brought food to the men of the house, father and sons, who squatted on grass mats to eat it. Ordinary Aztecs had no chairs; they sat on their haunches on a *petate*. The women of the family ate by themselves. Eating was a serious business; no one spoke unless Atox, the father, thought that his sons should be told something of great importance. And as soon as it was light the family, like all Aztecs in the great white city, were ready to leave for their fields.

Aside from religion and war, the most important thing in the life of any Aztec was his plots of land. Everyone, or almost everyone, was a farmer. Speaking Eagle never had to be reminded of this. He knew it from the moment he walked, and even before that his mother had carried him on her back to the cornfield, which they called the milpa. His first memories were of ripening corn and the corn song his mother sang as she worked in the field.

In the patio outside Speaking Eagle's house was a garden where his sisters raised flowers and hot chili peppers for seasoning their food. Canoe paddles were neatly hung on the wall, and the family's dugout canoe, also lashed to the wall of the house, rested in a small canal alongside it. Speaking Eagle's mother placed a gourd of water and a drink called *octli*, some tortillas and meat wrapped in a cotton cloth in the canoe. That would be their noonday meal. By the time Atox and his elder son poled their canoe out of the narrow canal, bordered by houses like their own, and entered the lake it was filled with other boats. All were going toward the mainland.

In the early morning light, the white city of Tenochtitlán seemed to float on the water. Thousands of gardens, filled with trees and flowers, spread around the flat-roofed houses. Many of these rested on *chinampas*, the basketwork gardens on which part of the city had been built.

Now the Aztecs did not have to depend on these floating gardens for food. They owned all the land for hundreds of miles around the lake. This land belonged to the clans, for no Aztec except the First Speaker could own land. All the land belonged to clans—there were twenty of them—and every piece of land was parceled out to members of each clan according to the number of people in the family. Speaking Eagle's family were six; they had been given six plots of earth, and this fact was written on the register books of the clan. The family did not own the land; they only had the fruits or vegetables that grew on it. When Speaking Eagle's father died, the clan would again loan his sons that piece of land. If a family had no children, the land would be reclaimed by the clan, who would loan it to someone else. It was ancient custom.

The corn was now fully ripened. Speaking Eagle knew exactly what work should be done at this time. He went through the fields, bending the ears of corn in such a way that the birds could not get at the kernels and eat them.

No one could remember a time when the Aztecs had not eaten corn, the plant they called *centli*. All the Indians had it, and they could not have imagined their world without it. They grew corn in milpas for two or perhaps three years in succession. Then, since their fertilizer was poor and the exhausted land yielded only stunted corn, they had to seek new fields. That meant that the clans and the tribe as a whole had to have considerable land in reserve so the old fields could lay fallow for a while. That was one reason why, as the city of Mexico grew and its people became more numerous, the Aztec made war on other tribes. They needed to acquire more land.

Almost everyone among the Aztecs was a farmer. Definitely everyone was a warrior. The Aztecs were farmer-warriors, Speaking Eagle's father would proudly boast. At the call of the war horn all Aztecs left their fields, hurried to their own clan meeting houses where weapons and shields were stored, and went wherever the battle raged. Still the feelings of the Aztecs were closest to the earth. They knew the soil; they knew the heavens; they knew when it should rain or when the winds would blow.

It was Indian custom to plant corn in March, after the rains. When the ground was soft, the Aztec dug out hillocks of earth, set three feet apart, in which he planted three or four grains of corn. Preparing the ground with only a fire-hardened digging stick was the hardest work of all, and the Indians habitually helped one another in this. As soon as the *centli* was a foot high, fast-growing beans were planted on the same hillock. Their vines entwined the cornstalk as it grew higher. Still later, squash was planted.

In April, rain fell heavily. As it was the rain god who granted this favor, it was custom to worship him and make sacrifices to him so the rain would continue to fall. In July the corn began to ripen, and then there were more festivals to the god. Now in the time of Speaking Eagle's work it was September, the time for harvesting.

Year after year, generation after generation, father taught son, and son taught son these things of the earth. For it was by bending nature to their will that the Aztecs had learned how to cultivate wild plants. In their early tribal life, they were forced to spend all of their time hunting wild animals or seeking wild fruits or grains in order to stay alive. They had no cities, but moved across the land constantly in search of food. Now with the passage of time—much time—they, like other peoples, had learned to cultivate plants. This had given them leisure time.

Only recently the clan council had discussed how much land each Aztec needed to provide for his family and how long he must work to harvest his crops. No one had fully agreed with all the others, since not everyone could work at the same pace or with equal intelligence, and the land itself varied in quality from place to place. But the council did agree that if one acre of land could be expected to yield 20 cargoes of corn each year—a cargo of corn was 60 pounds, which a man could easily carry on his back—and each man had ten acres, then each family in the clan would have 12,000 pounds of corn a year.

All this was figured out on paper by a scribe. To prepare the land, weed and harvest the corn (and the beans and squash planted on the same land), would take 200 days of an Aztec's time, provided his wife and his children helped him.

The other 165 days in the Aztec year that were left were the Aztec's "leisure" time. During that time he had to make his own sandals, his earthen jars and dishes; his wife and daughters had to spin cotton, then dye it and make the clothes for the whole family. Taxes had to be paid.

Naturally, the people had to pay for the upkeep of the city, its canals, waterways and dykes, and festivals which were held every month of the year, often many days of each month. The temples that gave them pleasure had to be maintained; the ball courts where the ceremonial ball game was played had to be kept up. All these had to be paid for. There were also Aztec warriors stationed in many parts of the land, and while they were gone others had to tend to their cornfields and see that their families did not want. This too had to be paid for.

The Aztecs did not use money. No one in ancient America had it. In place of money, they used a barter system and traded goods. One Aztec might trade corn for beans, or honey for sandals; another who brought shells from the seacoast traded them for something else of value. The same system was used for paying taxes. As there was no money, each Aztec paid in work service. If the high council decided a road had to be built, each clan furnished its quota of men from the clan for the work. Every time this was done, a scribe noted it down on a register. Each Aztec also had to give a portion of his harvest to the state each year. The Council of Four, the old men who guided the Aztecs in all ways, received the taxes.

There were some people who were not farmers. These were feather weavers, goldworkers, silversmiths, architects, writers, sculptors, artists, and the priests. Their time was given entirely to producing beautiful and useful works for the state. The contribution that each Aztec made each year went to them. In this way the non-farmers were rewarded for their work.

As Speaking Eagle turned down each ear of corn so the crows would not eat of it, he thought about all that corn meant to the Aztecs. It had given them leisure time; it allowed them time to think of other things than their stomachs. Because it could be stored and kept year after year, they did not have to worry about having food during years of famine. Corn! Everything in their lives circled around it—the days of the year, the festivals, their religion, their wars. Corn! That little nothing which was everything.

And now once again, as it had been for century after century, it was the gathering month, the harvesting of the corn.

Overcome by his thoughts, Speaking Eagle tenderly placed on the ground a small clay image of Xilonen, the corn goddess. Scooping up a handful of the good earth, he let it run through his fingers as he muttered his prayer, until the image was entirely covered.

THE MARKET

THE weekly market began before the stars melted away with the heat of day. People filled the causeways leading to the city; people filled the canoes which moved toward the city. Everywhere, within and without the city, there were people moving toward the market.

The Atox family, as all the others, rose at dawn to ready themselves for the market. As their clan district was near the main square, they had only to follow the great road that led to the center of the city. This causeway, called that because the greater part of it was over water, began at the town of Itzalalpa and extended on the mainland more than three miles straight north to the city of Mexico. The road was so straight and the great temple in its center so tall that it could be clearly seen from miles away. The causeway was twelve feet wide and within the city proper it was flanked by houses on both sides. Everyone who entered the city had to pay for the use of the road, as people do elsewhere in the world. At the entrance to the city Aztec warriors stood to take the toll, which the people paid with some token from their produce. At every fifty feet or so the causeway was intersected by a small canal, each one bridged by a wooden bridge that could be removed. This was

44

done for defense as well as to allow for the passage of larger dugouts.

The houses that lined both sides of the road and extended deep on either side were mostly one-storied houses. The better ones were made of brick fashioned out of a soft volcanic ash which was coated with cement painted a brilliant color. Most of these had no windows and the only entrance was from the small canals which flowed by most of the houses. Here, the people tied their dugouts. They stepped from the canoe into a small patio to enter the only door of the house. The Atox family had such a house.

At the end of the causeway, in the center of the city, was the great square. The Teocalli, the god house of the Aztecs, stood in the great square. This pyramid was over 200 feet high and towered above everything else. This was the way it was planned; everything else was dwarfed by it. One hundred fourteen high stone steps leading to the top of the pyramid were cut into one side of it. At its summit there were two large

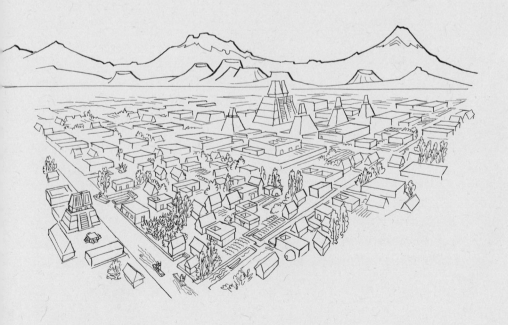

temples. In one of them the sacred fire could be seen smoking. It was never allowed to go out except at the end of the year, on the five empty days of the Aztec calendar. Priests, wearing long dark robes reaching to their ankles, moved about the temples. It was here that the priests beat the drums every morning to announce the birth of a new day; it was from here that they sounded their conch horns to stir the people to fight the battles for another day.

All about the Teocalli were other temples and palaces, ball courts and markets. The great square was so large that its center took up more than one tenth of the city itself. The more than fifty buildings in the plaza made up the religious, administrative, and social part of the city. The square spread almost across the width of the island, and water enclosed it on two sides. Around its edge was a frieze of snakes called Coatlpantli, or Snake Walls, because the mural represented one long continuous snake writhing itself about the limits of the square. It was painted green and red and measured 500 by 600 feet.

On the morning of the weekly fair, everyone in the Atox family was loaded down with the produce they intended to barter. The father carried a large collection of mirrors made from black volcanic glass which he had polished. Speaking Eagle and his brother had neatly rolled *petate* mats to sell, along with boxes plaited from the small grass fiber. His mother and sisters—all expert weavers—carried beautifully woven cotton cloths on their backs. Their slaves carried corn.

Not everyone owned slaves; they had to be purchased, and the price was sometimes high. Slaves were men who had been expelled from their own clan because they had committed crimes. They had no right to land, nor could they have the protection of the clan. They had lost their clan rights, so they were slaves. They worked in the fields, but they did not share

in the riches of the house. They slept in their owner's house
and were treated more or less like one of the family. There
was no fixed rule about how they should be treated; that depended on their owners. Girl slaves could get back their clan
rights by marrying free men. Speaking Eagle's father himself
had never treated them badly, for he told his sons to remember
that one of the greatest Aztec leaders, Itzcoatl, called Snake
Blade, was born of a free slave. Itzcoatl had risen by his merits
to become First Speaker.

Speaking Eagle's family, bent down with the weight of
things to trade they carried on their backs, joined the throng
of other Aztecs, all hurrying along like thousands of scurrying
ants. They crossed the wide canal, passed through the mural

of snakes, and turned left. In front of them was the pyramid-
temple. To the right was the great palace of Moctezuma, and
to the left, facing the palace, was the market. At one corner,
where the judges of the market sat under a great awning, was
the calendar stone. It weighed over 52,000 pounds and was so
large that anyone might wonder how it could have been brought
from the mainland across the wooden causeways.

The market, which all called Tiaquiz, was held every week. To be sure, there was also a daily market where people traded for their daily needs, but the big market, the one that drew people from miles around, occurred only once weekly. Many people, carrying their produce on their backs, traveled from places more than five days distant to attend it. Speaking Eagle's father, like most people, could tell at a glance the native lands of the various people at the fair. Each tribe had its own distinctive cloak. Some painted their faces with designs of circles and waves and decorated their greased hair with green-and-red parrot feathers. These people were from the hot lands on the

coast and near the sea. Those who arrived so bundled up that their faces could hardly be seen came from the cold lands. Their cloaks were simple, and their faces wrinkled as an old leaf.

Every product had its place in the market.

In one section, women sitting on *petate* mats with a small cotton awning over them sold live birds. Here were turkeys, lying quietly with their legs tied together, pigeons in small wooden cages, and parrots, owls, ducks, and quail. Next to them were the herb sellers. Old women who through long lives had come to know the value and the name of each herb or root or tree that grew in the land sold these from cotton bags. Herbs were the Aztecs' medicines; they used them as cures for toothache, for stomach ailments, for eyes that could no longer see as before, for cracked feet opened and blistered by so much walking. The old women had a cure, they said, for every disease.

Indians from the hot lands brought jaguar and puma skins, which they laid out for all to see. They had skins of the sea otter, too, and for those who could afford it, the skins of bats, sewn together so cleverly that they seemed to be a single piece of the softest cloth. They also brought live animals and birds for Moctezuma's zoo.

Next came the salt sellers. They were the poorest of all. They spent their time drawing salt out of the water in the lakes which surrounded the city. These people placed saline water in a shallow basin and allowed it to evaporate. Later they skimmed off the thin layer of salt that was left in the pan, put it into clay dishes, and sold or traded it at the market.

A great space was set aside in the market for those who sold corn and other vegetable products of the land. Naturally, this space was in great demand. An Indian who had beans to sell and wanted corn in exchange would sit down in front of one of the corn merchants, open his sack of beans, and offer them for inspection. The other fingered the beans, broke one, and ate it. If he was satisfied, he might offer half the amount of corn for the full amount of beans. Then the bargaining began. Each sitting with his sack in front of him, they would argue back and forth, sometimes raising their voices to such a pitch that it sounded as if they were angry with each other. If they were too loud in their business, a judge of the market would appear. The judges were there to see that there was fair dealing, and during the life of the fair they walked up and down the rows of the sellers and buyers. If there was a real dispute, they settled the matter right there and then. If people came to blows, Aztec warriors would hurry forward, and off to jail the offending one would go.

The Aztecs had no money, but they did know value. Value was what each thing meant to an Indian. An equal amount of corn had more value than an equal amount of beans because corn, which swelled when it was cooked, could be stretched to make many corn cakes; so corn had twice the value of the same amount of beans. Gold was much appreciated, so was silver.

The most precious thing the Aztec had was jade. A beautiful green stone, jade was found in the mountains to the south near Guatemala, and it was very scarce. It was considered good luck and its green was the symbol of fertility, for when a thing lived, it was green. When an Aztec died a small piece of jade was put into his mouth. He believed jade was his other heart, a heart of jade. All these things had value, without having money value.

Of late, cacao beans were being used as money. Cacao, from which chocolate was made, came from the hot lands. The dark seeds, three times the size of a black bean, were found in large pods growing out of the trunk of the cacao tree. To an Aztec, the most wonderful drink he could have was chocolate; it was an Aztec passion. First the brown cacao nut was toasted, then it was ground to a powder, mixed with water, and flavored with honey and the vanilla bean, which was steeped in it. Just before it was drunk, women beat it with whirl sticks until it frothed into foam. Moctezuma used to drink hundreds of glasses of it a day. It was rare because the cacao seeds had to be carried on the backs of Indians from a great distance. Some people used them as money; a thing could be purchased "for so many cacao beans."

The cotton market attracted many and these were mostly women. Women were the weavers of cloth, and cotton was a luxury. Speaking Eagle's mother went to this section with her daughters. She paid for her space by giving the tolltaker some cotton yard she had spun. Together, they arranged their weavings on the *petate* and sat down to await a buyer.

Before the Aztec had cotton the women used the fibers of the maguey to make cloth. This plant, almost as useful as corn, was found all over Mexico. It stood as high as a man, and its leaves were thick, green moist pads with long sharp thorns, like needles, along their edges. In fact, the Aztec women used these thorns for needles. When dried and combed, the maguey pads yielded long coarse fibers that had great strength. By splitting them and combing the fibers, the weavers could make a strong thread which they used to weave cloaks and breechclouts for the men and pull-over dresses for themselves. Maguey fibers were also used for rope, handles, and hundreds of other articles for Aztec houses. The maguey plant was important to the Aztec for another reason, too. Inside the thick hollow stem was a sweet syrup, the honey of the maguey. By gathering this and allowing it to ferment, the Indians could make *octli*, a strong beer. Maguey was so important to their lives that the Aztecs gave it a special goddess.

Cotton would not grow in the high country of Mexico. It was not until the Aztec conquered other tribes in the warmer valleys and settled in them that there was enough cotton for their needs. Cotton cloth, once a luxury, soon became a necessity. Now all in Mexico wore mantles of it.

Cotton was brought to the Aztecs as tribute yielded by some of the 371 tribes subject to them and traded to all the people. First it was carded, then spun into delicate fibers by means of a hand spinning stick, a process all girls knew by the time they were eight. Then the cotton strands were dyed.

Dyes were made from vegetables or from the natural dye of certain sea animals. Red came from the seeds of a tree called annatto; carmine color came from the insects which the Aztecs bred like cattle on the pads of cactuses. Black dye was obtained from the seed of the genipa tree. All these natural vegetable dyes were on sale at the market. When the cotton thread was dyed, the women wove it into garments for their families. There were no factories; weaving was done at home by the women in their spare time.

In Speaking Eagle's house there were three looms. They were back-strap looms, called that because a belt across the weaver's back held the woof of the fibers taut while the weaver worked. One of Speaking Eagle's first memories of his mother was of seeing her weave during the hours of leisure. Naturally she and her daughters made more cloth than they could use, and this was sold at the market. Every market day, the day of the Tiaquiz, she took her same place on the same *petate* and waited for those who would buy or trade for her cloth. And as her work was known for the beauty of its colors and the designs of animals and birds she wove into it, people always came first to her. In this way she could get more raw cotton; this way she had the means to buy pieces of jade, live turkeys or ducks, and all the other things that made life more pleasant and livable.

There were all sorts of things to trade for at the fair. Paper was piled up high for people to buy and make into things; there were dealers in gold and silver, which they offered in transparent goose quills. Others sold feather weavings, in which the quills of small feathers from rare birds were woven into cloth in such a way that the effect was a mosaic of plumes. They were expensive, and all warriors liked to have shields covered with feather weaving. Other Aztecs were craftsmen who worked with beautiful stones. These offered turquoise and green stones in wonderful mosaic patterns.

Dishes and bowls of earthenware were arranged in long rows. Earthenware was fashioned of clay, painted, and then baked in fire to make it as hard as metal. In this part of the market one could obtain any type of bowl one might want or need, ranging in size from the smallest, whose cup was only big enough to hold a hummingbird's egg, to great jars, so large that a full-grown man could stand inside of them.

In another corner of the market, food was offered for sale. There all the foods already known to the Aztecs as well as food that was new and strange to them could be had. And if you wished your long black hair washed, there were barbers to do this, too. They washed it with the roots of the soap tree and perfumed it with oils made from sweet-smelling flowers. You were shaved with razors made from sharp black obsidian glass.

Barbers were only for the very old, however. Most Aztecs had no facial hair, for hair on the face was considered very ugly. By nature, Indians have very little facial hair, and Aztec mothers put hot cloths on their young sons' faces in order to stunt or kill the few hair follicles that someday might grow. And if one offending hair appeared, it was quickly plucked out. Yet, for some reason which no one knows, as Indians grow older, hair begins to grow where it never grew before. Old men filled the barbershops.

At high noon, when the sun was burning hot and the vendors took refuge under their cloth canopies, the merchants, or *pochteca*, arrived.

They had been expected and eagerly awaited, for their arrival was a show that was part circus, part religious procession. The column entered the market at the side of the calendar stone. In the forefront, warriors blew on conch shells which boomed like muted trumpets. There followed wild animals in cages carried on poles between the Indian carriers. Then came jugglers, naked except for a loin cloth and awesomely painted with purple-and-red patterns. They threw large logs in the air and deftly caught them. The people murmured with astonishment until one of the logs fell and a humpback, half the size of a full-grown Indian, running on short bowlegs, quickly picked it up with one hand. The log was balsa wood

and almost as light as air. The Indians laughed at their own credulity.

Then came the *pochteca*, walking slowly and with great pomp. Each merchant carried a curved stick, and their mantles, tied at the shoulder in Aztec fashion, were beautifully woven and made of the finest materials. Indians walked in front of them with fans to keep away the insects, and behind them in a long line, walking so close as to seem like a long writhing snake, were the human carriers. Everything arriving and departing from Mexico was carried on the backs of Indians, for the Aztecs had no pack animals. Each Indian carrier had 60 pounds of cargo on his back, which he carried by means of a strap that went around his forehead.

The merchants were just returning from the southlands,

after being away for many months. They had come from the fabulous lands of Guatemala laden with cacao, jaguar skins, birds alive and dead, cotton dyes, jade, and emeralds. All "foreign" trade was in their hands. The merchants had their own guild, and membership in it was handed down from father to son. They had their own living clan section, and they paid no taxes. They had their own gods, and they answered to no one about their conduct within or without the land of the Aztecs.

Their carriers transported the goods the Aztecs made in the city—obsidian mirrors and knives, metates on which to grind corn, mosaics of brilliant stones, pieces of jade beautifully carved and polished—to "other lands." In exchange for these, for feather weavings and for pans of salt, the merchants received the goods made by the people of the "other lands."

In the late afternoon the people began to pack and to prepare to leave the market. They would return to their homes and prepare to visit other markets beyond Mexico. These markets were held on different days, spaced far enough apart that an Indian might visit one and then the other to sell, to barter, or to buy.

When the market began to lose its interest for him, Speaking Eagle walked over with other boys of his clan to watch the warriors practicing at *tlachtli*. The game was like basketball, and the goals were rounded stones with holes through their centers. In the villages where they did not have a stone court or such a stone, the boys practiced by making a hole through a basket. The great playing court stood in front of the pyramid-

temple. It was rectangular and shaped like an "I." In the center of the long court, set on a wall fifteen feet above the playing court, were the rounded stone "baskets." A goal had to be made with a vertical shot, not a horizontal one, which was the way the boys learned to play. Above and around the whole *tlachtli* court were seats for spectators. One end of the court was decorated with fearful-looking snakes of stone; there Moctezuma sat when he was present.

The game was played with a hard rubber ball about the size of a small melon. Because the rubber ball had to be butted through one of the stone holes, the warriors played with their elbows, knees, and hips protected with cloths. Making a "basket" was a great feat.

Tlachtli was very ancient. It went so far back in time that no one knew who invented it. It was played from Honduras to Central America, in the lands below the Maya, and far, far north for a thousand miles up to Arizona. The rubber came from the hot lands, from the Olmec people, said Speaking Eagle's uncle. Perhaps they had invented the game. All claimed to, but in truth no one knew. When the warrior players left the great court, the boys swarmed into it, and catching up an old rubber ball, tried to do what they had seen the players do. Finally, someone knocked the ball over the snake wall of the court into the canal. Speaking Eagle ran, vaulted the wall, and reached into the water for it. When he retrieved it and stood up, he found himself looking into the face of the great Moctezuma. Surrounded by his guards and leaning on their arms as was the Aztec custom, he was walking to the market to see what the merchants had brought from the hot southlands. For one terrified moment Speaking Eagle looked into his face; then as custom demanded he lowered his head and eyes to the ground. Moctezuma passed by and walked on toward the Teocalli.

THE MONTH OF THE BROOMS

IF ONE did not know which month of the eighteen months this was, it was because one was blind. Women were busily sweeping out their houses with brooms made from rushes that grew around the lake. They were cleaning their houses for the festival of Ochpaniztli, the Month of the Brooms. It was time for the reception of Toci, the mother of the gods, whose symbol was the grass broom with which the earth was swept.

The Atox family's house, the house of Speaking Eagle, had been thoroughly broomed, and in a corner reserved for the gods there was an image of Xilonen, the young corn goddess. Speaking Eagle had bought her from a maker of clay images at the market and set her up in a niche in the wall. The goddess sat with her legs doubled back and with her hands lying lightly on her lap. Her headdress was simple, and she looked out on the Aztec world with a kindly expression on her face.

Not all the Aztec gods looked kind. Many, like Smoking Mirror, who had the claws of a jaguar for feet, had terrible faces. The rain god Tlaloc had a nose that looked like a writhing serpent, with a snake's teeth and an adder's tongue. Xilonen was different and seemed like one of the family. Speaking Eagle's sisters had put corn leaves and flags of colored paper around her altar.

The eleventh month of Ochpaniztli was an important one. The priests had to use all their magic to hold back the rains. If rain fell and turned to hail, it would ruin the corn harvest, for corn still hung on the stalks. The priests had to prevail upon the gods with all their magic to keep them from allowing it to rain.

Dancing had been going on in the great square for days. At sunset each evening the whole Atox family went to watch it and take part in it. Women and men holding hands formed a long twisting line of people. No one sang. The drums were silent. They moved only to the rhythm of the high priests who led them. All that could be heard was the slap of thousands of feet on the white stone paving of the plaza. This went on for eight days.

After that came the first sacrifice. A woman attired as the goddess Teteo, and wearing golden ornaments about her neck, slowly mounted the 114 steps of the temple. It was so quiet that one could hear the birds quarreling in the marshes. When she reached the top where the twin temples stood, one beside the other, black-clad figures came out of the inky darkness of the interiors. They laid her down gently on the round sacrificial stone and held her there. Then the sacrificial knife—a terrible, beautiful, and awesome weapon of black flint with a mosaic handle—was raised to the sun. With one stroke the priest slashed open her chest, seized her heart, and cut it loose. With great solemnity he walked to the edge of the stairway, looked down on the silently massed people below, and held the heart aloft to the sun.

A deep murmur ran through all the people. Some were weeping openly, even though it was not custom to do so at this time. This Aztec woman had given her life for them. She had given to the gods her most sacred possession, her palpitating heart. She was not a prisoner, nor was she from a different tribe; she was one of them and had voluntarily agreed to be sacrificed so that the gods would be moved to compassion and would withhold the rain until the harvest was gathered. Her head would be saved, and when the skull was white and polished it would be given the honor place on the skull rack which stood on a raised platform near the ball court. On it were hundreds of skulls of honored sacrificial victims, all hung neatly in rows on sticks.

The dance of the Knights of the Eagle and the Knights of the Jaguar brought an end to the sadness. Drums pounded and horns sounded as the first ones, some of them shaking rattles to keep the dance beat, poured screaming into the plaza. Behind them, carrying spears and shields, came the Knights of the Jaguar. They were the finest Aztec warriors. They were dressed in real jaguar skins, and their faces were enclosed in wooden masks shaped like the open mouth of the jaguar. The Knights of the Eagle followed them. They leaped into the air as if they would fly, like eagles. All were young men. Their costumes were of feather weavings made with eagle feathers, and their faces were encased in wooden masks made to look like the beaks of eagles. In their hands were spears tipped with obsidian; all carried shields. They went through all the motions of throwing their spears, then leaped up and down and to the side as if they were avoiding spears thrown at them in battle. Theirs was a warrior's cult, and only the most famous fighters could belong to it. They had their own palace in the great plaza and many miles away at a place called Malinalli they had their own secret city; some of the buildings were carved out of the living rock.

They danced and fought the air all about the square until they came to a halt in front of a low-lying platform, twenty-four feet square, that had fifteen steps leading to it. On top of that was a smaller round disk, a complete circle, the symbol of the sun. In the center was a pole and tied to it by only one leg, leaving him free to move within the width of this circle, was a warrior. He was naked except for a loincloth. On one arm he carried a shield; in his hand he held a sword. Everyone knew that all the sharp obsidian had been removed from the sword. He was armed with a harmless wooden weapon, and he knew what he had to do.

This warrior was a famous chief of the Tlaxcalans, traditional enemies of the Aztecs, who had been captured in a recent battle.

Now his time had come, for here facing him was a Knight of the Jaguar. He too had a shield and sword, but his were real; the edges were fixed with flint knives so sharp that a warrior could cut off a head or an arm with a single blow. This was to be a gladiatorial combat, a mock battle in which there was no doubt who would win. The captive would die, as all the rest, for the gods.

But why must one die for the gods?

It is a question that man seems to have asked since the beginning of his time on earth. Man died, the Aztec priests would explain, so the demanding gods would send rain for the crops or halt the rain when it was not needed, prevent earthquakes, or stop the pestilence.

Aztec gods were like people. They had feelings like men;

they were quick to anger and slow to love. So they had to be appeased; the people had to give to the gods the most precious thing that man possessed—his life. And the most precious thing of his life was his heart. This was the food of the gods.

But how did the gods speak, and how did the priests know that this was what the gods wanted? The question could not be answered. No one really knew, and it was best to leave the unknowable to the priests who seemed to know what the unknowable wanted.

The Aztec tried to control or direct nature. To each element —the skies, the sun, the rain, the thunder, or to death or life— he gave a god, and each had its own name. Since he was a farmer, the Aztec knew that nature moved in rhythmic cycles. The rains usually came in certain seasons; the sun appeared at a certain time each day of the year. The planets, such as Venus and Mars and others, made their orbits in regulated time. The Aztec knew all this and passed it on from father to son. Even before they had writing, the people were aware that something happened "out there." Later, when the Aztec could read and write, all this was set down in books by the priests. All the things that man always dimly knew, they put down in their books.

The rhythms of nature and the coming and going of the planets were written down so that the priests, who studied the books and who knew the workings of the calendar, could tell at what time each thing would happen. They kept a constant vigil. They even knew, they said, which god controlled which force of nature.

The important thing was to know when to make an appeal to the gods and to which god the appeal should be made. If the sacrifice was performed at the wrong hour, the god they were trying to influence would not receive their offerings.

Therefore the priests studied the heavens and watched the movements of the planets so they could work it out on their calendar.

Blood was very important to the Aztec. That which had blood lived; that which had not, died. So the Aztec believed that even outside of the body, blood had power. It was like magic. When the priest offered the blood of a victim to the invisible gods, he was offering them power. If an Aztec did something wrong against himself or against his clan, he cut his ears or his legs and offered his blood to the gods to protect himself and others against that wrong. That was the reason for sacrifice. That is why the high priests cut out the heart of living people and offered it to the gods. Blood was the highest good.

When a person was to be sacrificed he was many times decked out in the image of the god. He was supposed to personify, *to be*, that god. Before the ritual of sacrifice every effort was made to make the person go willingly to his death. He should be moved by truly religious feeling. It was considered very unlucky if the victim held back or faltered. It was not considered good manners.

A warrior in battle never tried to kill; he tried to capture the enemy. The more prisoners he captured, the more he was honored. For the prisoners were held to be sacrificed to the gods. And why they and not the Aztecs? Because one could not expect that the Aztecs would offer themselves for sacrifice. If they sacrificed themselves, there would be none left. No, that was for other people. On one occasion, when the great temple was dedicated, the Aztecs sacrificed 20,000 people.

Sacrifice was not murder. The Aztec was horrified by murder. It was very antisocial. If one Aztec killed another, he would have to pay for it with his own life.

Sacrifice was a spiritual act for the Aztec. Man was only bowing to the will of nature. People were never just slaughtered for the sake of the gods; everything about the sacrifice was ritual and religious.

If mankind was to survive, man must beg the gods to allow him to live. And the gods must be fed to wax strong. Every Aztec knew that the gods did not really eat human hearts; they ate them symbolically. This part was hard for Speaking Eagle to understand, but then . . . But then, much of life was strange and no one could be expected to know everything.

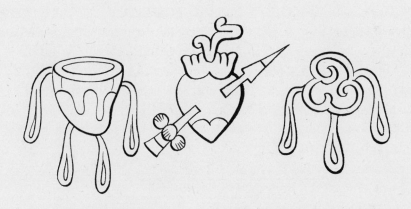

The Month of the Brooms, the eleventh month of the Aztec year, ended on the nineteenth of September, and the last sacrifice took place toward evening of that day. This ceremony was in honor of Tezcatlipoca, or Smoking Mirror, the god who was the god of the night and much more. He had various guises, and he was more feared than loved. To this god a sacrifice was to be made which moved to tears all of the Aztec people who witnessed it.

The priests brought out the most handsome of the prisoners. He was beautifully dressed in feather robes and a feather headdress, and for half a year he had lived as a god. His keepers had taught him to play songs on clay flutes which they gave him, and during that time he was surrounded by servants who did his bidding. On this day, the day of his death, he had gone all about the island playing soft music on his flutes. Now he marched with his servants to the base of the pyramid-temple. The moment was at hand. Slowly the attendants removed all the fine raiment he had worn for the half year that he had acted as a god. Then with his flutes in his hand he began slowly to mount the stairs to the accompaniment of drums. As he climbed he played soft music on his flutes, the same music he had played in the city. When a song was done, he broke the clay flute and let it fall. Then he took up another flute and continued playing. In this way he reached the top, leaving behind him on the stairway, the broken flutes, symbols of his past life. Then he was seized, and the sacrifice was made.

All this was for the gods.

THE TRIBUTE

THE time of tribute followed the harvest almost as naturally as night follows day. With the new corn harvest stored away and with time now for things other than work in the milpa fields, the Aztecs were on the move. Now it was the time for tribute collection.

The Council of Four met with Moctezuma and brought him the tribute charts. On them were painted the names of the 371 villages and tribes that yielded tribute to the Aztec. On the left side of the chart were the names of the villages, painted in rebus writing that looked something like a coat of arms. Beside each name was a picture of a temple falling over and burning; this meant that the village had been taken by Aztec conquest. There was also a picture of the particular ruler of the Aztecs under whom the conquest had been made; close to that was the date of conquest. On the next page of the chart was a list of the type of tribute each village had to yield to the Aztecs every six months. Corn, beans, arrows and shields, jade or gold, spears and feathers—it was all marked down on the chart so there could be no mistake, and alongside each item was listed the amount due. These amounts were written in symbols; a dot or a finger meant one, a flag meant twenty, a feather was

69

20   400   8000

400, and a bag symbolized 8,000. The tribute chart was so clearly written that any Aztec who could read pictographic writing could easily tell the name of the town, when it was conquered, and what tribute it had to yield.

The Aztecs depended on tribute. Although they worked hard, were very industrious, and carried on trade all over Mexico, still their luxuries depended on tribute. From the very beginning, the Aztecs needed more land for their people. Yet most of the land, the good land, was occupied long before the Aztecs arrived at the lakes of Mexico. So they had warred on other tribes to get land and when they had enough land, they found they wanted more of the good things of the earth. So they made war on still other tribes.

There were many different tribes throughout Mexico, and all were enemies of someone else. The Aztecs wanted to trade beyond Mexico, south of Guatemala, and beyond. They wanted to build roads through all these lands, but the other tribes stood in their way. So before they made war, the Aztecs sent ambassadors to these lands to discuss the matter.

The ambassadors arrived with great pomp, accompanied by slaves who fanned away the flies, and women who prepared their food. Warriors with painted faces and gold-studded earrings marched beside them. The Aztec ambassadors sat down and began to powwow with the chieftains of the tribes they were determined to conquer peacefully or with war. They bragged of their cities, their temples, their trade. They tried to impress the others with the number of their warriors. The chieftains answered in the same terms. They recalled that their tribe owned this land when the Aztecs were only beggars. That they had writing and temples when the Aztecs were empty-handed as monkeys. This kind of talk went on for many days and as many nights. Then, finally, the Aztecs stated their terms.

If the tribes would yield peacefully and without war, they could become part of the Aztec commonwealth. They could keep their own language. They could keep their own customs. The Aztecs would build a road through their lands, which would be protected by Aztec warriors. Every year their chief-tains would come and live for a few months in the city of Tenochtitlán. They could keep their own gods, although the national Aztec god must be set up in their temples with the same honors as their own. But they would have to yield tribute, whatever products they cultivated or manufactured. If not—war.

The chieftains knew what the Aztecs meant. If they said No to the offer of inclusion in the commonwealth, the Aztecs would come down on them like a horde of angry wasps. They well knew what the end would be. Whether it took a week or a month or a year, the Aztecs would never let go until they won. Then their men would be captured and carried off by the hundreds to be sacrificed to the Aztec gods. Many tribes gave in without battle, but just as many fought. Still the end was the same—the Aztecs always won. And on the tribute list were 371 villages and tribes who had to yield the things of their land to Mexico.

The tribute was collected every six months by official tax collectors who were aided by the men of the clans. It was now the turn of the Yopica clan to gather the tribute. Boys whose fathers were on the council of the clan were allowed to go, too, in order to gain experience. In this way Speaking Eagle, who had never been much beyond Anáhuac—the lakes of Mexico— went with his father to the southlands.

The morning was as clear as rock crystal the day the journey began. First, Speaking Eagle and his father went to the great plaza where they greeted the *calpixques*, or tax collectors. As these men were nobles, their lower lips were pierced and from them hung a pendant of jade. Their ears were also pierced, the lobes so enlarged that a goose egg could have passed through the hole, and in this hole they wore golden earplugs. Their hair was cut and greased and stood up like the neck hair of a wild pig when it is frightened. They wore a kind of turban around their heads. Their robes were woven with the richest decorations, and each of the four men carried a walking stick very wonderfully carved. The handle of each stick was a snakehead with a tongue of cornelian stone in its open mouth and eyes of jade. Since the tax collectors had no superiors except Moctezuma, they were proud and arrogant. They stood erect and apart from all others. Each had a nosegay of flowers which he sniffed from time to time as if the people who surrounded him were ill-washed and foul smelling. Slaves fanned them with feather fans to keep away the insects attracted by the odor of their hair grease. Near-by, there was a great line of waiting Indians, naked except for their loincloths. Warriors carrying shields and lances and with eagle feathers in their hair stood by. All their shields bore the coat of arms of the Yopica clan: a reed, four dots, and an eagle's talon.

The warriors were first in the order of march; then came

Atox, councilor of the clan, and beside him walked Speaking Eagle. Behind them marched the slaves, belaboring the air to keep insects away from the *calpixques*, who walked as if they were lords of the earth. And so they seemed. Behind them, half walking, half trotting, were hundreds of Indians who would carry the tribute on their backs.

The road made by the Aztecs was level. When it crossed small rivers, steppingstones were placed in the water so the travelers' feet would not get wet. There was a shrine to the gods every ten miles along this road, and every twenty miles there was a rest house where the travelers slept. These houses, like the houses of the Indians outside the city, were made of sun-baked brick with grass roofs. The walls were neatly white-washed. Inside on the mud floors were *petates* for sleeping, and at one end of the house was a kitchen where women prepared foods. Each village whose land touched the road was obliged to keep up its section of it, and the people of the village had to see to it that there was firewood and food in the rest houses. It was part of their work tax. In this way each village shared equally in the task of road building and maintenance.

The first day of the journey south, the expedition came to Cholula. They did not enter the town, for the road turned just outside it, but Speaking Eagle could see the large number of houses it had and the many clan temples rising above the flat-roofed white houses. He saw, too, the great pyramid—the Temple of Quetzalcoatl—that rose so high the Mixtecs called it Man-made Mountain. It was, his father told him, the tallest pyramid-temple in the Mexican land.

They continued along the road to the south. All along the way it was carefully kept up, just as the first part of it had been. At ten-mile intervals there would be a shrine. In the niche sat Zacatzontli, god of the roads. Every day the tribute collectors burned a piece of copal, an amber-colored resin, before him and prayed for a good journey. At night, after a day's journey of twenty miles, a rest house.

All of this land and its people were completely new to Speaking Eagle. The Indians in the villages were of tribes he had never seen before. Some wore their hair long and painted their faces red and black; others tied their hair on top of their heads and tattooed their faces. Many did not speak the Aztec language, and the collectors had to speak to them through interpreters.

The Aztec language—Nahuatl—was very ancient. Speaking Eagle presumed that everyone in all the great land of Mexico spoke it, but he soon learned that this was not true. Nahuatl had been the language of the ancient Toltecs. Most of the Indians who lived around the lakes of Anáhuac spoke it, but beyond the valley each tribe had its own speech. Sometimes it was so different that there was not a single word that resembled Nahuatl. The appearance of the villages differed too. The manner of building houses was different from that of Tenochtitlán, and even their gods had different names. At one time every tribe had been at war with some other tribe, so that there was no peace over the land. When the Aztec conquered he made the people stop the small wars, and roads were built connecting their villages. Aztec warriors kept the peace.

For the first two days of the journey the land looked very much like that around the lakes. Corn milpas were scattered here and there where the land was fertile. When it was not, the people grew the maguey plant on it.

By the fourth day the road began to climb, and the travelers soon found themselves among giant pine forests where the trees were so tall and so many that they hid the sun. This was the lair of the eagle, and its nests could be seen in the high branches of the trees. Around the base of these trees, widely scattered, were the bones of the animals the eagles had eaten. Many of the trees were marked, the bark cut deep around so that they would die. Even as they passed, Sleeping Eagle saw Indians hacking at the trees with stone hatchets. In two years the girdled trees would die, and then it would be easier to fell them. Such great trees were pulled all the way to the city of Mexico by means of wooden rollers and ropes made from maguey fibers. Canoes, too, were made of them, and Speaking Eagle was reminded by the deep smell of pine wood that the ceilings of the temples were also made from these trees. On the fifth day, which meant they had walked 100 miles, the expedition left the pine woods and began to go down to the hot lands. They had entered the territory of the Zapotec.

These Indians were a very proud and fierce tribe. Twice they had been conquered by the Aztec, and twice they had rebelled, killing the Aztec governors. About the time Speaking Eagle was born they had rebelled again, and his father had been one of the warriors sent to wage war against them. It was a long war and no one surrendered. Atox had been wounded in the leg

by a spear, and he still limped because of it. It was many years before the Zapotec were fully conquered. Even now they gave up their tribute reluctantly.

Before the travelers lay the valley of Oaxaca, a valley as flat as a corn cake. The land was checkered with fields under cultivation. Pumpkins and squash, cacao trees, and vanilla orchid beans were cultivated in this warm valley only 3,000 feet above the level of the sea. It was a rich land. On the hills were temples and plazas, so many that Speaking Eagle lost count of them. For centuries they had been the houses of the gods of all the Indians in the valley. Now they were neglected; weeds grew out of the stones, and the frescoes on the walls were scarred by time.

At the city of Mitla the Aztec tribute collectors were met by the chieftains of the land who had been notified in advance of their coming by a runner, sent ahead of the main group to bring the message to the Zapotec. The chieftains looked wonderfully well in their cotton robes. They bowed three times to the *calpixques*, touching the earth each time with their fingertips.

Mitla was different from any place Speaking Eagle had ever seen. The temples did not stand on high pyramids as did those of the Aztec. They were low, and the designs of the stone decorations on the walls looked like those used in weavings. In one of the palaces a *petate* had been spread on the floor, and wooden chairs, reserved only for great leaders, were brought to the *calpixques*. At a word of command women brought them chocolate and beat it with whirl sticks until it frothed. The tribute collectors ladled it into their mouths.

The next day the collection began. The tax collectors set their faces to look fierce; not for a moment did they relax. The scribes brought out the tribute roll, made of *amatl* paper as pliable as the softest skin. On it was painted the history of the Aztec conquests. There was the date on which the Zapotec had first been conquered, the year of 7-Reed (1467). There was the picture of Moctezuma, called the Wrathy, who was the grandfather of the present Aztec leader. Close to it were the coats of arms, the symbols for the Zapotec villages, and what they had to yield as tribute, or taxes. Since dawn Zapotec Indians had been bringing in corn. It was rolled into *petate* mats, each bundle weighing 60 pounds or what a man could carry on his back. As the sacks were brought in, the Aztec scribe noted them down on the tribute roll. Then came the cacao beans—also wrapped in *petates*—then cotton. One town in the jungle had to pay its tribute in jaguar skins; these, too, were brought in, 400 of them, as given on the tribute chart. All day long the tribute poured in. Each item was checked off on the chart; then it was loaded on the backs of the carriers, who were sent on ahead. It would take them eight days of marching to get back to the city of Mexico.

The *calpixques* now asked for Zapotec Indians to carry the rest of the cargo to the Aztec capital. As this was not on the list, the Zapotecs protested. They seemed to forget they had been conquered; they talked rapidly and loudly as if they were not in the least afraid of the collectors. They knew what sending their men to the Aztec capital might mean. They might never come back. They would be held for sacrifice.

For now, all over the land, the uneasiness of the Aztecs made itself felt. Rumors about the strange ships on their shores traveled throughout Mexico. Recently there had been an armed clash between the white strangers and Indians in Yucatan. The strangers had used a weapon that roared like thunder and spouted like lightning. It was terrifying. Could this be the Plumed Serpent God returning to Mexico as he had said he would? Did he return with new weapons?

The Aztecs, having the most to lose, worried most. They sought the answer from the gods, and to make them answer they increased human sacrifices. The conquered tribes expected to give tribute to the Aztecs, for this was the law of the land. But they were not willing to give up their youths to be sacrificed to the Aztec gods.

At last the tribute was collected. It included everything that the Aztecs did not have, or at least, did not have enough of: cotton, 800 man-loads; cacao and vanilla beans, 400 man-loads; hundreds of animal skins, bird feathers, shields decorated with the insignia of the Yopica clan (their clan reward for doing the work of the tribute journey), war costumes, *huipillis*, or women's pull-over dresses, beautifully woven. All of this was destined for Mexico. So did the Aztecs enrich themselves.

The dreaded days over, the Zapotecs prepared to give their formal farewells to their protectors—and destroyers. No one said what he really thought. The Zapotec leaders wished immortal life to the great Moctezuma. The tribute collectors haughtily thanked them for their hospitality—and their tribute —and began to move off.

Far ahead, the long line of human carriers was already winding up the hills that would lead to the great pine forests. The very last of the *tamenes*, the carriers, were preparing to lift their loads when they were halted by Speaking Eagle. They followed him to where his father lay in great pain. A cure-doctor leaned over him, blowing tobacco smoke on his face to frighten away the bringers of witchcraft. Had he been be-witched? This was the first question the cure-doctor asked Atox, but he was too ill to know. His forehead broke out in a great sweat, and his lower limbs shook. The fever of the hot lands had settled in his bones. He could not move.

There was a hurried conference among the Zapotecs. They did not want him to remain. For what if he died? The Aztecs might say that they had poisoned him. It would be best to be rid of him, lest he die in their land. They searched for their strongest Indian, and wrapped Atox securely into a strong net. Other Zapotecs lifted him and suspended him from the head-band of the great-limbed warrior. Then half running, the carrier and Sleeping Eagle made for the end of the long column.

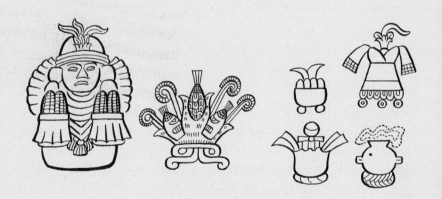

THE DEAD AND THE UNDEAD

A CHANGE had come over the Atox household. Where once the girls danced on the hard mud floor to the flute playing of Speaking Eagle, they now only talked in whispers. None of the other clan people visited them as they used to when the night shadows settled down on the city. Everyone knew, or thought they knew, the reason. The house of Atox was bewitched.

The cure-doctor had come again and again. He was there now. Speaking Eagle hung back in the shadows looking at the sick man. His father had changed much since his return from the land of the Zapotec. His naturally bronze skin was pale, almost as pale as one already dead. He ate little. He perspired constantly and kept calling pitifully for water, which they gave him from a gourd. The cure-doctor brought every remedy that he knew, but still the disease that held Atox was not released. Before the cure-doctor put his medicines to the test, he first purified the ill one by blowing tobacco smoke across him. Then he began to search for the fairy dart, the "stone" that caused the illness.

The Aztecs believed, as all believed in early Mexico, that disease was caused by a "someone," not a "something." Someone, wishing a person ill, caused a dart or a stone to be

81

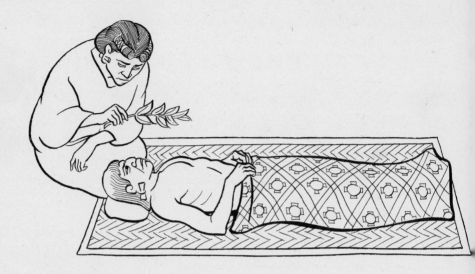

lodged in his body. Someone had fever sent down from the the mountains, carried on the winds by the wind god. Someone had Tlaloc, the rain god, bring ulcers or foot sores; others, gods of the night, brought blindness. Or someone could— many did—employ people versed in witchcraft to bring illness and death.

First the stone had to be removed. The cure-doctor rubbed the body back and forth like a masseur. He was living up to one of his names: "he-who-recovers-the-stone." The stone was always found. Speaking Eagle saw the cure-doctor put the stone in his own hand. This he accepted; it always happened. And why? People believed in it, and the cure-doctor was only following custom.

Once the stone was removed, medicine was given.

Old people knew the plants; they knew those that cured strained eyes, or those that cured a cold. The cure-doctor had a book of herbs, an herbal, to help his memory. In it were pictures of each plant and the pictograph telling its name. The drawings were so accurate that Speaking Eagle, looking over the cure-doctor's shoulder, could recognize plants he knew. The book was many-paged and filled with plants whose virtues the cure-doctor was supposed to know.

Each day he arrived with the plants that were painted in the herbal. Some he ground into powder and blew into the nostrils of the ill one. Others he steeped in warm water until the water was dark with the color from the plant. These were generally ill-tasting. Atox obediently drank the infusion even though it

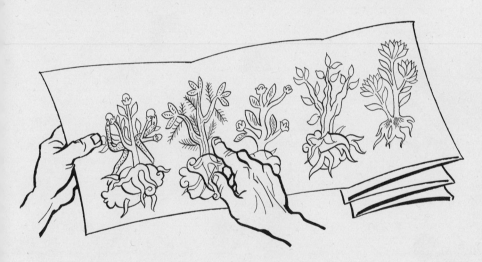

was so bitter that his stomach could not hold it. Then the cure-doctor brought the plant given to those who were fear-burdened, who were sick from fear and not from witchcraft. All these availed nothing. There was no doubt, since the disease did not yield to the cure plants, that it must be caused by magic, by the unseen powers. Magic was now tried. Atox was put through all manner of hocus-pocus, but never once did he protest. It was not good custom. He must not protest. If he did so, his plaints might spoil the magical powers. Still nothing helped, and now death was upon him.

The cure-doctor came for the last time. He turned to the last pages of his book, looked at the pictographic writing, and began to read aloud.

"The *ticitl*, the cure-doctor, will draw his conclusions as to whether the patient is to die or to get well from the eyes and nose . . . a mark of death is the sootiness found in the middle of the eyes . . . eyes that grow dark and are unseeing . . . Also there is the ever grinding of the teeth . . . and the babbling of words without meaning, in the way of parrots. You may anoint his chest with pine wood crushed in water." And as he spoke this, the cure-doctor did what the book told him to do. "Or you can puncture his skin with a wolf's bone, or with an eagle's talon." The cure-doctor followed in action that which he read in the book. Speaking Eagle's father did not even open his eyes. "Now hang close to his nostrils the heart of a falconet wrapped in a deerskin." There was little response to this, and the cure-doctor slowly got up off the *petate*. He began to put back into his jaguar-skin bag all the things of his profession— pipes, tobacco, balsam, bat wings, eagle talons, cactus needles, a swordfish snout. Reading once more from the book, he said, "The fatal necessity is at hand . . . death will soon follow."

The Aztecs believed that dying was antisocial. Although they knew that everyone died sometime, still the act of dying was considered to be of great harm to the clan. They thought that one never really died. They believed that life and death were only aspects of the same thing. When one died, one became a member of the unseen powers who could do harm as well as good to the clan. The Aztec always thought of himself as part of the clan. He lived, worked, and fought as part of the clan; he had no life outside of it. Now dying would change this; he would be outside of the clan.

The *tonalpouqui*, the sorcerer, came at Speaking Eagle's call. As were all those who were considered wise, he was old. He had seen life in a thousand ways. He wore the insignia of the sorcerer; his lower lip was perforated and filled with a piece of gold. When he was younger he had worn large golden ornaments in his pierced ears. Now he was an old man and he did not bedeck himself any more like the young nobles. His ear lobes were empty of ornament; the cut lobes dangled loosely like a tapir's snout. In his hand was the sacred roll. This he unrolled before the dying man and began to study it to see if he died under a lucky sign or an unlucky one. He blew tobacco smoke, and with an incense burner he blew the white smoke of burning copal across him. That was the smoke sign of the gods. First the dying man had to confess.

Everyone confessed; every Indian who lived in Mexico had the same custom. The dying were supposed to confess. Did they hold anything back? Did they know what was causing the disease? Perhaps they had not honored the gods, perhaps they had committed a social sin, perhaps they had not respected a taboo. If they confessed, it would neutralize the effect of their dying and the clan would know what to do to wash away the uncleanliness. In the Aztec world everyone knew that evil and good struggled to take over a man's soul. He must confess. He must not be the silent helpmate of evil.

What could the good man do? Atox was dying; he had not the strength to even call out the name of his elder son. From the time he was born, the clan, his people, his family, had done everything to help him escape destruction by the unseen powers. They did not name him until a lucky day was at hand. As he grew up, many tried to teach him what he must do and must not do. When he did an unsocial act against his clan— such as drinking intoxicant *octli* when he was not supposed to—he cut his ears and legs and offered his blood to the gods. Around his neck he wore an amulet made of a shell and an eagle's foot; it was a lucky charm to help him ward off the "evil" ones. He never did anything unless he consulted the calendar or the horoscope to see if the time was right. But somewhere along the way of his life he must have forgotten something; somewhere he must have forgotten to salute or show devotion to the gods. Somewhere, somewhere, somewhere . . .

Speaking Eagle sadly flexed the legs of his dead father into a sitting position. Then he secured the legs and arms, and they were tightly bound. Next, his mother and sisters brought a piece of newly woven white cloth. This was to be his shroud.

Now into his mouth they put their finest piece of jade. This was the symbol of his heart—a heart of jade. He would need this to deposit with the gods on his way to Mictlan, the abode of the dead. The body was sewn into the cloth.

Outside, in a large square put aside for that purpose, a large funeral pyre was prepared. The body was placed on it, and around it they put the things of Atox's life: his shield, his sword, his finest tunic. His wife, now his widow, prepared corn cakes and beans for his journey; bowls of a freshly made drink were made to slake his thirst. Nothing must be left out; the dead must be made content. For in reality, the dead were not dead, they were only un-living; and being lonely, they might want to carry off someone of the living to share their loneliness.

The dead were the undead. They were the unseen members of the clan. When they passed into the state of the undead they at once had much power. And it could be for bad or for good. So the living must secure the good will of the recently dead.

If not, he could haunt them, and the whole clan could be harmed by it. The dead might bring bad luck to the clan. There might be an epidemic of disease, or the corn might not ripen in time. Or even worse, he might cause an earthquake and shake down the houses of the clan, his family. So nothing must be omitted from the death bundle, and the *quacuilli*, the priest of the clan, came to see that everything was included in it. This priest could easily be identified. His long black cloak was decorated with skulls embroidered around the fringe; his hair was matted with blood from the sacrifices.

Then the death bundle was cremated. The fires were lit, and the family sat down to wait the end. They cried and sang sad little songs.

> *Where shall you go?*
> *Where shall you go?*
> *Is yours the road of the double gods,*
> *Will your home be in the place of the undead?*
> *Will it be inside Mictlan?*
> *Or only here on this earth?*

The ashes of the dead man were put into an urn. The jade, the heart of jade which had withstood the heat of the fire, was placed on top of the ashes. If one's name was great among the Aztecs, the urn was placed in the temple. If one were, as Atox, a member of the clan council, it was placed in the Tecpan, the clan meetinghouse.

An Aztec believed that he was immortal. To him death was only a form of life. Life and death had the same reality. The departed went to those places presided over by the gods who had protected them in their lifetime.

In the Aztec underworld there were thirteen heavens and nine hells. Where one went had nothing to do with how well one lived life. Heaven or hell was not a reward. The places to which the dead went were determined by their occupation in life. Warriors went to the place of Tlaloc, the rain god. Those who drowned went there also, for this god was also the god of water. Everyone had his afterlife arranged by what he did. Those who were unclassified went to Mictlan. The souls had to wander over high mountains, go through heat and cold, until they reached the abode of the Lord of the Dead. When they reached the seventh hell, they had to leave, as a pledge of good conduct, the piece of jade, which the living had put into their mouths. When they reached the end of the journey they were placed in the ninth hell.

And how the living?

Speaking Eagle and his family went into mourning for eighty days. There were certain foods which they could not eat. They could not drink intoxicating *octli*. The women had to cut off their hair. The men or boys could not put eagle feathers into their hair. They must not hunt or fish. Food and drink had to be taken regularly to the urn that held the dead man's ashes. They had to cut the lobes of their ears and slash their legs to offer blood as sacrifice. At the end of the eighty days they could resume their normal life, but for four years at regular intervals this period of mourning had to be repeated.

MARRIAGE: THE TYING OF THE TILMANTLI

SINCE man must live, life goes on. For no matter how heart-rending is one's grief, only time—which nothing can hurry—makes things anew.

This must have been Speaking Eagle's thought throughout all those gray years, the four years of ritual grief. Then one day it was over. His father's soul, in whichever of the thirteen heavens or nine hells it was, had reached its final destination. Speaking Eagle was free. He was now eighteen. He had come to his majority in death. It was March of the year of 1-Reed (1519).

Speaking Eagle had made up his mind to be married. During his four-year vigil over his dead father's soul, when his life was confined, he often went to the market. There one day he saw a girl. She was only sixteen, yet this was the age of marriage for girls. Speaking Eagle thought she was very pretty in her *huipilli*, which hung down from a V-cut at the neck. Her house, he learned, was in the clan district of Pochta, and her father was a *pochteca*, one of the merchants who traveled beyond Mexico. By one of those secret ways which is known only to love, he made his feelings known to her. He was often seen with her. He went to her house, worked in it, spoke when spoken to by her father, and told him of his journey to Oaxaca. It seemed that her family was not entirely displeased with him.

Marriage for the Aztec was not a simple affair. First, even though one's clan might have as many as 20,000 members, marriage had to be outside of the clan. Since everyone in the clan was considered related to everyone else in the clan, a young man had to seek his bride elsewhere. A man's marriage was not his business alone; it was everyone's business. Speaking Eagle's mother thought him too young to marry and that he should wait until he reached the age of twenty, the age at which most Aztec men married. But since Speaking Eagle had played the part of a man since his father's death, he wanted to be one all the way. Speaking Eagle had to appear before the clan council.

One entered the clan when one was born. The clan gave land to till, it gave its protection, and the old men gave their counsel. It provided a school for young boys and girls. These rights a clan member never lost unless he stole, murdered, or did something else against the clan. Marriage also belonged to the clan. Anyone who entered the clan by marriage would have these rights, too. The council must be certain who was entering the clan by this means. Clans were jealous of each other, too. They must be careful that a woman, under the guise of marriage, did not enter as a spy. Anyone in love could laugh at such questions. But they were serious ones, and Speaking Eagle had been taught to treat them seriously. These questions had to be asked.

The priest of the clan brought the Book of Fate, which contained a count of the 260 days in the sacred calendar. It was written in books of folded paper and filled with pictographs which recorded the lucky and the unlucky days determined by the movements of the stars and planets.

Having been told by his uncle what he must say and what
he must know, Speaking Eagle first gave the council the date
of birth of his bride-to-be. The priest then looked to see if
the dates of their births and fates were harmonious. Every
member of the council knew that to have the daughter of a
powerful *pochteca* married to one of their own clan was a very
good thing. Still, custom was custom.

Having secured the council's permission, the next step was
to get the consent of the girl's father. The council selected two
old women to bring gifts to the father and to secure his consent.
This was the way all Aztec marriages were made. Naturally,
the father refused. It was the custom. He must always refuse
the first visit and the first offer. Back came the old women and
talked and talked, as old women do. Speaking Eagle was urged
to augment his gifts to the bride; he collected the jade—his
most precious belonging—and sent this. His mother and sisters

prepared the most beautiful weavings. Once again the old
women went to the Pochta district. Once again there was much
discussion. Finally, after a long period of give and take, all the
parties agreed.

On the night of the wedding the old women, who were the
matchmakers, went to the home of the bride and carried her
to the Yopica clan building where all Speaking Eagle's relatives
were gathered in the large council room. Speaking Eagle and
his bride, Morning Star, sat on a grass mat in the center of
the room. The guests drank *octli* made from the fermented
sweet syrup of the maguey plant. Finally, an old man came
forward and tied the edges of their cloaks, their *tilmantli*,
together. This act symbolized marriage.

Then each of the old people began to talk in turn. They talked of virtue, of custom. When one finished, another began and talked of duty and the need for children. So it went on for several days while Speaking Eagle and his bride, still tied together, sat on the mat and looked at each other.

When this part of the ceremony ended, the couple was separated for four days. Each went his own way, but during this time neither was expected to eat. One could drink only when parched with thirst. When all this was done, they met again and entered their house together. A new life cycle was beginning.

At first Speaking Eagle and Morning Star lived in his father's house. Then, as was his right, he received from the clan a small piece of empty ground on one of the small canals. He began to build his own house of stone, as befitted a man whose family had always sat on the clan council. One day Speaking Eagle, too, would be a person of rank.

Before his death Atox had gathered together a large amount of cut stone and for many years it had lain piled in the patio of the house. This stone was really volcanic ash which in the thousands or even millions of years since it had stretched out over the plain had been pressed into stone. It was easy to split and easy to cut. Out of this cut stone Speaking Eagle built his house, cementing the pieces together with a mixture of clay, earth, and lime.

Every Aztec man knew how to build his own house, just as every woman knew how to cook and weave. Everyone had to be self-sufficient as a farmer, builder, and craftsman. "An Aztec," Speaking Eagle's father used to say, "must be complete. If he is not, he perishes."

So Speaking Eagle, helped by his clan brothers, built his own house. Aztec society was co-operative, and they came willingly to help. One day one of the men who helped Speaking Eagle build his house would need his aid, and Speaking Eagle would return his clan brother's favor. Selfishness was considered very poor manners among the Aztecs. So the house went up. As was custom, it was windowless. Speaking Eagle got the wooden beams for the roof by trade. On it he put flat tiles which he made himself. Like all Aztec houses, it had a patio where flowers or small food plants were raised, and in time there would be a tree. The patio faced a canal where the dugout canoe was tied. A new life cycle had begun.

The milpa in which Speaking Eagle had worked when he was a boy had now been passed on to him by the clan council. He would work it as his father had worked it, and when his children came they would help him just as he had helped his own father in the same field.

Would not such a life go on forever? Would not the great Aztec tribe, which now held every tribal village under domain, continue on and on? No one doubted it. But in the fourth Aztec month, the Month of the Long Fast, the strange ships on the ocean-sea appeared again. For days runners, carrying messages between the coast and their leader, arrived and departed. This time the messages said that the bearded strangers had landed. There had been another battle with the people near the sea. . . .

Now, once again the temple fires began to smoke. And once more captives mounted the 114 stone steps of the pyramid-temple.

A strange and uneasy feeling began to fall upon all the people.

THE BOOK OF FATE

WHAT did the stars mean as they hung in their balance in the sky? Why did the priests watch them so carefully? And why did the Aztecs always have to consult the Book of Fate before they did anything?

Speaking Eagle began to wonder about these natural questions. Most Aztecs, it is true, never asked them. It was enough to them that they were; they did not seek to know how they came to be or why they must do what they did. It was different with Speaking Eagle. He was curious by nature. And besides, his father and his father's father had been members of the clan council. There was no doubt that some day he, too, would be on the council if he proved worthy. Although the Aztec leaders were always elected, it was Aztec custom that the leaders should come from the same families if they proved themselves worthy. Speaking Eagle's uncle, his father's brother, was a member of the clan council. He felt that the time had come for Speaking Eagle to be present at these meetings. It was time that Speaking Eagle studied the stars, the planets, and the Book of Fate which recorded the count of the sacred days. He should also know about writing and how to read the picture characters that were painted on the books of folded paper. And he must know how the clan operated.

97

Now each clan, or *calpulli*, was a division of the tribe. When the city of Mexico was founded in 1325 there were seven clans; now in this year 1-Reed (1519) there were twenty. Each one was separated from the other clans, or wards, of the city by a wall or boundary line, and each elected a chief who was called a *calpullec*. (The Nahuatl word *calli* means house, showing that a clan, or *calpulli*, was, in the Aztec mind, only an extended number of *callis*, or houses. The clan, or *calpulli*, was like the cell in a beehive; so many cells made up the tribe.)

The leader of the clan was aided by a council of old or distinguished men. They advised the chief of the clan and saw to it that the land the clan owned was fairly distributed to all the families in the clan. They had large paper books in which every piece of land was registered. They knew how much corn or beans or squash each man took from his land.

The land did not belong to the man who worked it, but the harvest of the land did. Of this each Aztec had to give a part, perhaps one tenth, as taxes. In addition to this, each Aztec had to pay his work taxes. If a bridge was to be built, then each of the twenty clans had to furnish equally so many men for the work. If an Aztec warrior was away for the wars, then those of his clan who remained behind had to help cultivate and harvest his crops, so the family of the warrior away on duty would not want for food.

Each clan had its own temple, built like the Teocalli in the great plaza, but much, much smaller. Each clan also had its own meeting place, the Tecpan. Here the council met and here, too, were storerooms for corn, beans, and other crops which the clan would need during a drought or a bad harvest. And here were stored the weapons for war—lances, slings, swords, quilted cotton armor, shields, and helmets. Each clan had a totem, or symbol, of the clan. A war chief could always tell which warriors came from which clans by looking at their shields. The schools for the young boys and girls were also located in the Tecpan.

The *calpullecs* of each clan formed the great council of the First Speaker. Each one represented and spoke for the people of his clan. Always present at these meetings were also four of the oldest and most experienced men of all the tribe. These men, known as the Council of Four, were appointed from the four great parts of the city which corresponded to the four cardinal directions. They were the councilors of the ruler. Usually they were related to him, being his uncles or grandfathers.

The First Speaker was elected by the Council of Four. He was always a noble; that is, his father or his uncle or his grandfather had been First Speaker before him, but one did not become the leader just because one's father had. One had to earn the right. If the sons of the previous leader were not worthy, the council would look down the line for another. The present First Speaker, Moctezuma II, was only the nephew of the previous king, but his grandfather had been the famous Moctezuma the Wrathy, conqueror of all southern Mexico down to Guatemala.

Moctezuma II had been a warrior, and a very good one. Then he became interested in the stars, in the Aztec calendar, in wizards, and in foretelling the future. He had been sent to the school for priests, where he learned to read and to draw the pictures that were the Aztec form of writing. Like other students, he had to do menial chores. When he was elected ruler, those who went to tell him of his great fortune found him half-naked, sweeping down the steps of the great pyramid-temple.

Now he had been King of the Aztecs since 1503 and he

walked the earth proudly. He was treated almost as a god. No one was allowed to look at his face directly. When coming into his presence one had to bow three times from the waist, touching the ground with the fingertips. And when one withdrew from his presence, one had to bow and bow and bow until out of sight.

He had one wife, a very beautiful woman who was the daughter of a great chieftain of another tribe, and by her he had several children. He also had numerous other women about his palace. These waited upon him, bringing him food in golden cups and water in a silver service to wash his hands. They wove his robes, which he would not wear twice in succession. His sandals were of gold, and when he went out he was carried in a litter decorated with jade and gold, pearls, and the golden-green feathers of the quetzal bird. Still he rose every morning at four o'clock, the same hour as did all the Aztec people. He went to the courts where the old men presided to see that all his people were treated equally and that justice was given. If he found any official doing wrong, he was given worse punishment than the others. All Mexico grew great with Moctezuma. Never had it been so large or so rich. There were now over 60,000 houses in the city of Mexico. Since each family had an average of five people, the population of Tenochtitlán was about 300,000!

How did the Aztec know this history so well? By the records they kept, for every detail of their history was set down.

Speaking Eagle saw now how important it was for him to study Aztec writing, to learn how to form the symbols and pictures which were their letters, to make words, and then be able to read them. In the Tecpan of his clan there were writing-painters, so whenever he had time Speaking Eagle sat down by the painter to be instructed.

These men, called *tlacuilo*, usually learned the science of writing from a priest. When an artist became a master he was called a Toltec, the name of the long-ago people who were famous as artists a thousand years before Speaking Eagle was born. This painter sat on his haunches and drew on *amatl* paper the same kind of symbols and picture-writing that Speaking Eagle had seen when they gathered the tribute at Oaxaca. As he worked, the *tlacuilo* explained to him how an artist must feel.

The good painter,
  Toltec artist of the black-and-red ink;
   creator of things with black-ink water,
    —must have understanding.

He must have god in his heart.
  He must draw things with his heart,
    and he must have speech with his own heart.
  He must know colors, apply them, and shadow them.
  He draws feet and faces,
    he sketches the shadows,
      tries to do it and does it so—
        He will be called a Toltec—a master.
          He paints the colors of the flowers; he paints
            with god in his heart . . .

The artist also explained the meaning of the pictographs he drew on the paper. These signs, for example, were the symbols for precious materials. Some of them—the mosaic, for example —were realistic; the mosaic showed a series of stones put together. The other signs were accepted by agreement. The head priest might have said, "Let this sign stand for gold," and the writers had agreed. Ever since that time it had been used as the sign for gold. All the villages in Mexico had a name symbol. Now everyone knew that the sign of a towering peak meant *tepec*, or hill. If a house or village was set upon a

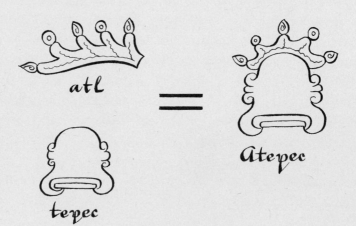

atl

tepec

= *Atepec*

hill, it would be named Caltepec; if a village was located on a hill where a great deal of rain or water (*atl*) fell, it would be called Atepec.

Writing was not an Aztec invention. Many people in the land of Mexico had had it before them. The Maya, who were among the long-ago people but who lived still in Guatemala and Yucatan, had had writing for two thousand years. Everyone had it; the Toltec, who had disappeared long ago; the Mixtec; everyone in central Mexico.

Numbers, too, had their symbols of value; a finger or a dot was one, a flag meant twenty. No one knew why, but it did.

A symbol which looked like a feather, but which the priests said was a hair, meant 400; a bag with a cross was the symbol for 8,000.

The most difficult writing both to understand and to draw were the portraits of the gods. There were many. All had different faces; all had different meanings. It was important to know one from the other, for if the wrong portrait of a god were placed in the book or the priest mistook it, he might make a sacrifice to the wrong god at the wrong time. That

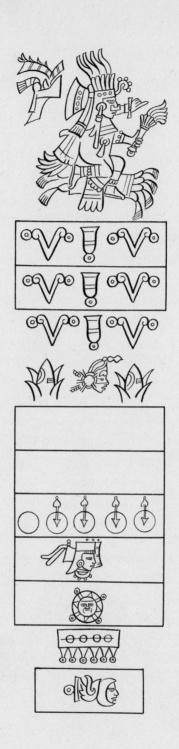

which was intended for one would go to another. One god would be angry because he did not get the attention due him; the other would be angry because he had been mistaken for another.

First, and above all, there was Huitzilopochtli, the Hummingbird God, the Sun and War God. He was the chief god of the Aztec. Then came Smoking Mirror, chief of the whole Aztec pantheon of gods. Next the Plumed Serpent God, Quetzalcoatl, god of learning. There were more than a hundred gods, including the creative god and the gods of rain and moisture.

The signs of the day were simple. They were easy to draw and to read because they looked like the things they represented. Who could mistake a house, or a snake with its tongue hanging out of its mouth, or the face of a spider monkey or an eagle? There were twenty such day signs; there were eighteen Aztec months, each of twenty days, which made 360 days. There was no sign for the five empty days, the *nemontemi*, at the end of the calendar year. They were all unlucky days. They had no symbol, and they had no count. When the end of the year came the Aztec put out the fires all over Mexico and waited to see if the end of the world was coming. When they saw the sun and the morning stars rise after the five empty days, they knew that life would go on. Everyone hurried to the sacred fire, the only one kept burning. From this they lighted their torches, and the city took on life again.

Still, why did the Aztecs watch the stars so intently? Why did they make the movement of them into a calendar?

First of all, because they were farmers. Since time began, man had noticed the effect of the moon on the tides; if he lived away from the sea, he saw the effect of a new moon. At night when he watched the stars he noticed that those which appeared at one place during one season were gone during another. He learned in time that nature moves in a pattern, in rhythm. He learned that these changes affected him. The long-ago people had made all this into a calendar. The Aztecs inherited it and added to it; they tried to discover just what these rhythms were. If they could control them, they felt that they could control the rain and perhaps the world. If not, nature and the gods that controlled nature were capable of destroying the Aztec and all the other people of the Mexican world. This was why the Book of Fate and the count of days were kept.

In time Speaking Eagle understood something of the calendar. Each month had a pictograph of the day sign. There were eighteen months. The first began on February 12, and was called the Want-of-Water month. It ran until March 3, which was twenty days. Others followed until eighteen months of twenty days each had passed. The year ended on February 6. Then there were the five empty days, the *nemontemi*, which made 365 days. This was the solar calendar.

In addition to this, there was the sacred calendar, the Book of Fate. It was called *tonalpohualli* and had a period of only 260 days. This calendar also used the Aztec day signs—the pictographs of the house, rabbit, snake, eagle, and all the rest. But the sacred month had only 13 days.

Every movement in the heavens was noted by the priests. It was important to know when the planet Venus completed its turn around the earth, when there would be an eclipse of the sun, and when the moon would be shadowed by the earth. All this affected the people. As Speaking Eagle well knew, nothing of a serious nature was undertaken unless one first consulted the horoscope. A child could not be named unless

the planets were "right." A woman would not begin to make a jar of clay unless the day was right, for fear the clay would break. No war chieftain started a campaign unless the lucky days were at hand.

The more Speaking Eagle listened to all this, the more his head spun with numbers and dates. The *tlacuilo*, or painter, was very patient; things such as these were not easily learned. He tried to make it simple. He removed two wheels from a toy his child pulled along the ground. On one he painted the day signs of the 365-day solar year, the eighteen months of twenty days. On another he painted the day signs of the 260-day year which had twenty months with only thirteen days to each month. These two calendars he put together like a cogwheel. When one turned, the other turned so that the young man could see how the sacred calendar of 260 days was related to the solar calendar of 365 days. He showed Speaking Eagle that when these two were joined together they made two dates (for example, 7-Rabbit, 2-Crocodile) which could never be confused with any other date. Those two dates would not be repeated until fifty-two years had passed. That was the great cycle.

These cycles had much to do with the influence of the planets, the moon, or the stars on man. If a man was born in the year of 5-Reed, he would be a merchant; if he was born in the year 7-Eagle, he would have heart trouble. Every day had been studied by the priests and astronomers to determine if it were lucky or unlucky. That is why they looked at the stars and were so careful that a newborn child should be named on the fortunate days.

Now this year 1519 was an unlucky year. Consider the things that were happening all over Mexico. A woman had borne a child with two heads; a river which had always been dry had suddenly flooded with water and drowned all the men who were walking on the dry river bed. And as for the rumors of those strange men with beards in strange ships that landed on the shores of Yucatan and went away and came back again . . . The Plumed Serpent God had prophesied when he went away from Mexico, so many ages ago, that he would return. He would return in the year of 1-Reed. The artist slowly turned the Book of Fate and called off the count of days. This year was irregular and could only fall in the years 1467 or 1519.

The Aztec knew all these things because they watched the sky. And all that they observed was put into these sacred almanacs.

Alone at night, Speaking Eagle looked up to the sky. He had always looked to it, for the thousands of sparkling stars made the night seem friendly. But now, stars were no longer just stars to him. In some way those little worlds held his fate. The stars would never again be just stars.

THE MEN IN IRON HELMETS

At the sound of drums at dawn the people awoke as they always did. But this time, on that remembered day in October, the Month of the Feast of the Mountains, there was another sound, a deeper rumbling than the drums. The earth shook.

Speaking Eagle joined all the others who crowded into the street. All faces were turned toward the snow-covered volcano Popocatepetl. It was in eruption. Flames shot into the sky, and sounds rumbled through the earth. Lava poured down its sides, melting the snow. Water rushed down in torrents into the lakes of Mexico. It had been years since "Popo" had erupted. Its twin, the snow-covered mountain, called Sleeping Woman because it looked like a woman sleeping under a cotton cloth, lay as it always did, sleeping.

Flames continued to shoot out of "Popo" even after the sun was up and they were no longer so visible. Later, the waters of the lakes rose. Large waves rolled down upon the city, and water came up over the bridges and lapped into the plaza.

This was only another one of the strange things happening in Mexico. There had been senseless talk for some time. People spoke of the column of fire seen every midnight in the direction of the east. Lightning had destroyed two temples, and someone had seen a comet, so bright that it could be seen

109

during the day, rush through the sky. One man had heard a woman's voice, speaking clearly and loudly in their own language, coming from the lake and saying, "My children, my children, we are lost—lost."

Then there had been the strange turkey brought in by a hunter from the jungles. It had, they said, a mirror on its head. This seemed so unusual that Moctezuma had come down to see it. When he first looked into it he saw the stars reflected in it, which was strange enough, but when he looked again, he saw bearded men marching. He sent for his high priest to look into this turkey-with-a-mirror-for-a-head and tell him what he saw. But before the priest arrived, the turkey broke the mirror and flew away.

These were troubled times. When the Aztec farmers went to their fields they spoke of little else. Everyone, it seemed, had something new to tell, something he had seen or heard.

One night when the farmers returned to the city from their milpas on the mainland, they could hear the booming of the great drum across the water. Even at a great distance from the city it had a deep sound, as if thunder was opening up a cannonade in the heavens. The streets of the city were filled with people. Usually at this time they would be at home, eating their evening meal, the largest of the day. Now they all moved toward the plaza. The sacred fires were brighter than ever, and the sound of the great wooden two-tongue drum was so loud that the Aztecs could not make themselves heard. The temple stairs were covered with blood from top to bottom, and the bodies of those sacrificed were still lying there.

All day Moctezuma had been at the temple. Those who knew him had never seen him so disturbed. Now, they said, he was shut up with his wizards, trying to unravel the latest information about the strangers who had landed on the coast and brushed aside the Aztec warriors as easily as if they had been a handful of flies.

In the middle of the night the clan council was summoned to hear Moctezuma's messenger. Speaking Eagle's uncle, carrying a torch of grasslike stalks dipped in tar to light his way so that he would not fall into any of the canals, went to the Tecpan where all the councilors were gathered. It was cold and the young attendants had lighted the braziers, large hollow containers made of baked clay in which charcoal burned. The flames and heat escaped through the vent holes on all its four sides.

The messenger and the old men of the grand council had

been sent by Moctezuma, who had left notice earlier that
evening that he should be wakened at any time news arrived.
It had come at eleven o'clock that night, brought by runners
who had traveled in relays from the coast 200 miles away.
They had brought a picture-history of what was happening
on the coast. A few hours later the ambassadors whom the
First Speaker had sent there in order to have a true report
also arrived. They were carefully sprayed with blood from a
sacrificial victim to purify them, and high priests came in to
blow copal smoke over them. Now they were ready to speak.
They had shown Moctezuma picture-writing. Now the old
chieftain unrolled the whole thing before the eyes of the
council of the Yopica clan for them to see and wonder at as
he told his story.

"First, they came in ships that have towers. Their skin is whiter than ours, and they have long beards and hair. They have thunder that speaks and when the shot bursts out of its belly, it gives a spray of sparks. The smoke smells horribly, and many of us felt sick at the smell. When the ball hits a tree, the tree turns to dust."

The artist had faithfully pictured all that the old chieftain spoke. The council could see the cannon, the sparks, the tree, the ships.

"As to the men, they are armed in iron, with iron helmets on their heads. They mount animals, which are something like our deer, only taller and heavier, and when they are on their backs, they tower roof high. Only their faces are visible from without the iron helmet. Some have black hair, some yellow hair. But they do not eat human hearts."

In the dimly lighted room, all the councilors, forgetting their dignity, crowded around the picture of these animals that looked like deer, but were horses.

"And as for their dogs. They are very big, with folded ears, great hanging chops, and fiery flaming eyes—pale-yellow eyes —and hollow bellies. Their tongues loll out; they are always panting; their hair is flecked with spots like a jaguar."

This was an amazing piece of information. The Aztec knew dogs; they were little animals, and some were hairless like those that come from the place called Chihuahua. Some Indians ate them; some worshiped them. Many Aztecs kept dogs in their houses as pets, but none of their dogs were like those drawn by the artist.

Moctezuma needed the advice of the council. What or who did they think these people were? Were they gods? Was their leader the Plumed Serpent God? He had said he would return to Mexico in the year of his birth, and this was now 1-Reed.

He had been against sacrifice and, as a test, the high priests had offered a plate of human hearts to the one who seemed to be the leader of these strange men, and whom they called Cortés. This man with the iron hat was shocked at the offering and knocked the plate out of their hands. Every test they gave him seemed to prove that he was the Plumed Serpent God— the one whose coming the Mexicans had awaited and dreaded. So what thought the council of all this?

The next morning a large group of high priests and nobles hurried over the great causeway, going in the direction of the coast. Human carriers, bent down with presents, accompanied

them. One carried a large symbol of the sun, as big as a wheel and etched with figures and symbols. It was of solid gold. Another carried a silver disk, as large as the golden sun. It also was beautifully etched with pictures and symbols, and was solid silver. Another carried a feather headdress the like of which the Aztecs had seldom seen. It was made entirely of the golden-green tail feathers of the quetzal bird that lived in the high rain forests toward the south. Each feather was over a yard long and as a bird could grow only two of these a year, it must have taken over 200 of these rare and beautiful birds to furnish so many feathers. The crown of the headdress was woven in beautiful cloth on which were sewn emeralds, jade, and turquoise. It was fit for a god, and to a god it was going. For Moctezuma had decided that these strangers were, indeed, the fabled gods returning from fabled lands.

"The Plumed Serpent God has returned."

THE COMING OF THE GODS

THE Aztecs waited.

Only those whose harvest had to be taken at this time went to the milpa fields. The others stayed in their houses, waiting . . . waiting . . . Still, work did not stop, for in their houses the people made pottery, or sandals of maguey fiber, or grass mats, or whatever they did best.

Speaking Eagle was a mirror maker, skilled in an art not many knew. He had learned this from his father. He searched the markets for large pieces of obsidian. This is molten rock, thrown up by volcanoes, which cools into hard, brittle black glass. The Aztec knew how to split the glass by applying a stone chisel to a slight crack or lesion in it. By hammering ever so slightly, the glass could be split in such a way that the resulting edges were as sharp as a razor.

Speaking Eagle's family had always been mirror makers. He knew how to clip and split a large chunk of the glass until he pried out a piece that was almost flawless. Then he began to smooth it, first with coarse and then with fine sand, until after weeks of work it was so highly polished that it reflected a face as if one looked into a limpid pool of crystal water. His family was famous for these black mirrors, and the art of making them passed from father to son. So it had been for generations. Now, with the Aztec world all upset by the frightening news of the strangers that were coming upon them, it was good to have something to do with one's hands. It filled the hours. It was better than just waiting . . . waiting . . .

The strangers were marching on Mexico. The Month of the Feast of the Quail had just begun—the month beginning at the end of October when the Aztec performed the ceremonial hunt for game—when the first terrible news came. There had been a battle at the sacred city of Cholula, and the strangers, suspecting an ambush, had attacked the Mixtecs. They shot off their cannons and killed many chieftains. Now one of the Mixtec leaders was here in Mexico demanding war upon the strangers.

"They are not gods. They are human. They can receive wounds and they can die," he said. And to prove it he had brought the head of a Spaniard—a grisly thing to see, with beard and matted yellow hair—as well as a head of the animal the stranger had ridden.

The war horns sounded. Out of the temple boomed the long-base horns, sounded only for war, and the sound was taken up by all the temples of each clan. Speaking Eagle, like every man in his clan, rushed to the Tecpan. He was an *iyac*, a young warrior, as well as a farmer. He was expected to fight, and since he believed that bearing arms was the highest honor, he was ready at once. The men were given their arms and put on their body armor, which were woven cotton coveralls, padded with cotton and soaked in salt-water brine. If the armor was well-made, it would resist an arrow or the cut of a sword. Then they got their *chimalli* shield. This was made of wood and covered with animal hide; over it was a feather weaving showing the totem, or badge, of the clan. The weapon the Aztecs liked best was the javelin, a shaft of smooth wood tipped with obsidian glass. With the aid of a spear thrower, a small device held in the hand on the spear shaft, they could throw it with great force.

In times of war each clan chose a captain who was chief only as long as the battle lasted. The Aztec warrior was hard and spartan. He had been trained for it since childhood, and could walk or run or trot for miles. He could carry 60 pounds on his back all day long without complaint. War was an honored state. The more enemies a warrior captured, the more he was esteemed.

Nevertheless, because of the nature of the land, battles had to be short. The Aztecs had no beasts of burden; they had to carry all their supplies on their backs. If the battle was not decided in a few days, they would have used up all their stones for slings, their arrows and javelins and food. They would be forced to return home, but they would come back again. Sometimes one battle was enough to win a whole war, for the Aztecs were the most ferocious warriors in all Mexico.

Few other tribes could stand against them. When they came on for battle the mere sight of them was enough to make the heart stop beating. The Knights of the Eagle in their war costume of eagle feathers and a headdress like an eagle's open mouth were fearful to see. So were the Knights of the Jaguar whose helmet masks made them look like jaguars. The other clans were painted in various colors; their shields hung together so that the marching column writhed like a serpent. Shouting so horribly that cold shivers ran up and down the spines of their enemy, they closed in. First, the sling throwers, whirling rocks as big as goose eggs, filled the heavens with stones that fell like hail. Then the bowmen moved up to shoot arrows into the enemy ranks, and under cover of this, the spearmen crouched forward and threw their javelins. At the same time other warriors, swinging their deadly *maquahuitl* swords, swept forward. The object was to rout the enemy and in the confusion seize their chieftain. When he was captured, the battle was usually over.

Now, as soon as the warriors of the Yopica clan were armed, they marched together with their captain to the great plaza. In front of the stone of Tizoc other clans were already gathered. Torches were burning, and the horns of war kept up the din. The stone of Tizoc was the war stone. It was circular, eight feet in diameter, and carved with scenes of battle. One of the carvings showed Tizoc, who had been First Speaker fifty years before, holding an enemy by the hair. That was the symbol of victory. When the battle was to be enjoined, all the captains came to the stone of war.

A fierce young man was walking back and forth on the stone. He was Cuauhtemoc, cousin to Moctezuma and the leader for the battle against the strangers. He was magnificently dressed. His headdress stood high over his head and was covered with quetzal plumes that moved and swayed as he strode back and forth, shouting to his people. In his hands he held a jeweled javelin which he raised as he spoke and made as if to throw at an enemy in front of him. He told of what the Aztecs would do to these people or any other people who invaded their country. He spoke of Aztec greatness. He spoke of Moctezuma, the First Speaker. He aroused the warriors to fighting fury.

Then, something strange happened. Out of the shadows came the Council of Four, the chief advisers of Moctezuma. They called Cuauhtemoc aside and talked to him in the shadows. Then the war chief left and one of the councilors came forward. Moctezuma and his wizards who probed the future had decided, he said quietly, that the strangers were gods. They believed them to be of the retinue of the Plumed Serpent God. Tomorrow, in the middle of the fourteenth Aztec month, the Month of the Quail—November 8, 1519— the strangers would enter the city. All of the Aztec people were ordered to receive them as they would a god. The strangers came to Mexico only to open up a new age of peace and happiness.

The next morning Speaking Eagle, like thousands of other Aztecs, was on the roof of his house, eager to watch the coming of the gods. In the distance he could see the strange bearded men riding their strange animals along the causeway that connected the Aztec capital with the mainland.

Not long before this the great Moctezuma had passed by to meet them. He was carried in a litter and attended by the nobles of his realm. There had been the Lord of Cuitlahuac, wearing a green emerald on his lower lip, and the Lord of Tacuba, who was so fierce that when he was angered he was said to weep tears of blood. All the Aztec witnessed the greetings of their First Speaker with the newly arrived gods.

Then the procession made its way down the main road which led to the great plaza, to Moctezuma's palace. When they came close, Speaking Eagle could see how different they were, and yet how much the same. Their hair, clothes, and weapons were different; yet the strangers had eyes and teeth like the Aztecs, and they smiled and chatted. Even if they spoke in a language no one could understand, they looked like men. First came their leader. He was bearded and had an iron hat with a white feather in it; beside him walked an Indian girl. Then came all the others, mounted on their animals. All the things that the artists had drawn in the pictures were there: the cross, the cannon, the crossbow, the blunderbuss, the iron swords, the great dogs.

The procession stopped for a moment right in front of Speaking Eagle. Looking up at him was a bearded man in an iron hat. He smiled, showing his white teeth, and waved.

"Get on, Bernal Díaz, get on," said another bearded man behind him.

And that same Bernal Díaz del Castillo, years later, wrote:

. . . who could count the multitude of men and women and boys in the streets, on top of the houses, and in canoes on the canals who had come out to see us. It was indeed wonderful.

Within two years, the whole of that beautiful city was destroyed by war. Speaking Eagle died with the other uncounted thousands of warriors who tried to defend it. It was a terrible war. The people who died were so many that the Aztec had no time for burial. Cortés explained to his king, ". . . yet seeing how they were so plainly determined to die without surrender as was ever a race of men, I knew not by what means . . . how to save ourselves and to avoid destroying them and their city . . . one of the most beautiful in the world . . ." On Saint Hippolytus Day, August 13, 1521, the last Aztec surrendered and the wonderful city of Tenochtitlán passed away into memory.

	AZTEC WORLD	CENTRAL AND SOUTH AMERICA
A.D. **1100–1200**		
1200–1300	Aztec peoples begin migration to Anáhuac, 1168 Toltec civilization declines Aztecs settle at Chapultepec	Maya civilization declines
1300–1400	Tenochtitlán founded in Lake Texcoco, 1325	
1400–1500	Itzcoatl (Great advancement of Aztec civilization) Conquest of neighboring tribes Causeways to mainland and temples built Moctezuma (I) the Wrathy Aqueduct built from Chapultepec forest Aztec territory extends from Atlantic to Pacific	
1500–1600	Moctezuma II (Aztec civilization at height) Conquest of Mexico by Cortés, 1519–1521 Tenochtitlán destroyed; Mexico City erected in its place, 1521	Amerigo Vespucci reaches Amazon, 1499 Inca civilization at height Spanish explore and conquer Caribbean and northern South America Pizarro conquers Peru, 1531–1535

	NORTH AMERICA	EUROPE	ASIA
A.D. 1100–1200		Crusades in Holy Lands, 1096–1270	
1200–1300		Magna Charta in England, 1215	Genghis Khan conquers all of central Asia and China, 1206–1221 Mongols overthrow the Arab Empire, 1258 Marco Polo at court of Kublai Khan in China, 1271–1295
1300–1400			Tamerlane ruler of Asia from Russia to Persian Gulf; Ming Dynasty in China
1400–1500		Renaissance Invention of printing, 1439	
			Ottoman Turks conquer Byzantine Empire and most of Asia; block trade routes to Far East
	Columbus discovers America; claims part of West Indies for Spain, 1492	Moors expelled from Spain; beginning of Spanish explorations in New World	
1500–1600	Ponce de Leon discovers Florida, 1512		Vasco da Gama reaches India, 1498
	Balboa discovers Pacific, 1513		
	(Magellan voyages around the world, 1519–1522)		
		(Turkish expansion into Europe stopped at Vienna, 1529)	
	De Soto discovers Mississippi River, 1541	Protestant Reformation	First Europeans visit Japan, 1542
	First city in U.S. established at St. Augustine, Florida, 1565		

BOOKS FOR FURTHER READING

Benitez, Fernando, *In the Footsteps of Cortés*. New York, Pantheon Books Inc., 1952.

Burland, C. A., *Magic Books from Mexico*. Baltimore, Penguin Books, Inc., 1953.

Calderón de la Barca, Frances E., *Life in Mexico*. New York, E. P. Dutton & Co., Inc. (Everyman's Library edition #664), 1913.

Collis, Maurice, *Cortés and Montezuma*. New York, Harcourt, Brace & Company, Inc., 1955.

Díaz del Castillo, Bernal, *Cortez and the Conquest of Mexico by the Spaniards in 1521*, abr. & ed. by B. G. Herzog. New York, William R. Scott, Inc., 1942.

———, *The Discovery and Conquest of Mexico*. New York, Grove Press, (Evergreen Books edition E-86), 1958.

Prescott, William H., *The Conquest of Mexico*, 2 vols. New York, E. P. Dutton & Co., Inc. (Everyman's Library editions #397, #398), 1909.

Shellabarger, Samuel, *Captain from Castile*. New York, Little, Brown and Company, 1945.

Spinden, Herbert J., *Ancient Civilizations of Mexico and Central America*, 6th ed. New York, American Museum of Natural History Handbook Series Number 3, 1948.

Vaillant, G. C., *The Aztecs of Mexico*. Baltimore, Penguin Books, Inc., 1950.

von Hagen, Victor W., *The Aztec: Man and Tribe*. New York, New American Library, 1958.

INDEX

125

ABOUT THE AUTHOR

VICTOR W. VON HAGEN's interest in the Aztecs began early in his career as an explorer when he spent two years in Mexico. That was 1931, and since then his many expeditions in most of the countries of Central and South America, the Galapagos Islands, and the West Indies have made him a recognized authority on the great Indian cultures of this hemisphere.

Mr. Von Hagen is the author of more than thirty books, including *Maya. Land of the Turkey and the Deer* and *The Incas: People of the Sun,* both for young people. These two, with *The Sun Kingdom of the Aztecs,* comprise his trilogy on the major cultures of the Western Hemisphere before the coming of the white man.

ABOUT THE ARTIST

ALBERTO BELTRÁN is a young Mexican artist whose artistic abilities and understanding of the ancient Indian cultures of his native land have already earned him a reputation as "the successor to the late Miguel Covarrubias." The Panamerican Prize, the highest distinction in the drawing division of the First Biennial of Painting and Drawing, was recently awarded him by the Instituto Nacional de Bellas Artes in Mexico. He is known in this country for his fine work in *In the Footsteps of Cortés* by Fernando Benitez (Pantheon) and *Aztec: Man and Tribe* by Victor W. von Hagen (New American Library). This is the first book Mr. Beltrán has done for children.